Yanqui, Come Back!

Also by the author
A SHIP CALLED HOPE

Yanqui, Come Back!

The Story of HOPE in Peru

WILLIAM B. WALSH, M.D.

1966

E. P. DUTTON & CO., INC.

NEW YORK

To Paul Felix Warburg
whom I was fortunate enough
to call my friend

FOREWORD

By the end of the summer of 1961, we of the S.S. *Hope* had closed the log on our maiden voyage and said good-bye to those wonderfully kind friends we had made in Indonesia and Vietnam.* But even while their satisfying farewells—"Thank you! Please come again!"—were still ringing in our ears we were posting to our next port of need. After a warm invitation from the Peruvian—North American Medical Association, the S.S. *Hope* was again at sea. Destination: Salaverry, Peru.

Our arrival there was hardly triumphant. *Yanqui, go home!* signs were everywhere, warning us to expect at least a skirmish if not a battle.

Winning battles is hardly the mission of a hospital ship, even though I have heard our medical staff referred to as one of America's most effective cold-war weapons. We had gone to South America, as we had gone to Asia, with no desire to foist any credo upon a people. We went to treat and to teach, to dispense medicine, not propaganda. The effectiveness of Project HOPE's approach is the story of this book.

There will be more voyages for the S.S. *Hope*, and I trust that from each one we, as teachers, will return with the same treasures of knowledge and friendship we brought back from Peru. I wish only that the reader, like all of us on the world's first peacetime hospital ship, will discover new meanings for the word "hope."

WILLIAM B. WALSH, M.D.

* The visit of S.S. *Hope* to Asia was documented in Dr. Walsh's book *A Ship Called Hope*, E. P. Dutton & Co., Inc., New York, 1964.

CONTENTS

ILLUSTRATIONS

[1]

Could I take another call?

Yes, I certainly could, and was delighted to find that an old friend wanted me to lunch with him.

"By the way," he added, after fixing our date for the Aviation Club just across from the White House, "a visiting physician from Peru will join us. I think you'll be interested in what he has to say."

This pricked my curiosity because the caller, Bill Thoman, had been a career foreign service officer in Latin America and was presently our liaison with the United States Information Agency, and a valuable advocate of HOPE.

HOPE, hlth orgnztn is the listing in the Manhattan Telephone Directory and in those of some fifteen other American cities where branch offices of Health Opportunity for People Everywhere have been established. Founded in 1958 in response to President Eisenhower's People to People Program, Project HOPE had grown from a personal dream into a flourishing, functioning organization. Our nerve center is the headquarters office on Washington's Wisconsin Avenue (from which I work as President and Medical Director) and our greatest pride of achievement is the hospital ship named, naturally, the *Hope*. Donated by the United States Navy, after service in World War II and the Korean War, the *Hope* had been fully equipped and enthusiastically staffed by volunteer doctors and nurses. Just a short time before Bill Thoman's provocative telephone call, the *Hope* had returned from a gratifyingly successful two-year mission to Indonesia and Vietnam. Not only had thousands of cases of disease and deformity been treated on the ship and affiliated shore-based clinics, but new techniques had been demonstrated to hundreds of local doctors and nurses in the Far East. Training, as well as treatment, had been an integral part of the Project's program from its founding as a voluntary, nonprofit organization with the sole aim of bringing health—and hope—to people everywhere.

Now, early in 1961, the *Hope* was undergoing much-needed repairs in her home port, San Francisco. We were certain that preparations for a repeat performance in some other deprived area of the world would soon be under way to follow what we of the Project could only regard as our triumph in the Far East. But almost before the *Hope* had docked, determined efforts were being made to discredit the entire Project. From my listening post in Washington—a city not unaccustomed to backbiting—I heard that false reports of our mission had been given to members of the new Kennedy government and that damaging tales of failure had been substituted for the facts in official files.

The same sort of maneuvering had gone on two years before, under President Eisenhower, so I was not caught unprepared. Furthermore, President Kennedy had written to me that he was "confident that the Project will continue to benefit the peoples of Indonesia and other countries of the world. There is no endeavor exceeding in humaneness and importance the prevention and cure of illness and disease. . . . Please convey to the physicians, nurses and others participating in Project HOPE my congratulations for the excellent work all of you have done."

When the President became aware of this new harassment

of HOPE, he sent word that any future plans we might have had the continued support of his administration. We breathed a sigh of relief, for no private program of this size can exist without the approval of our government; the *Hope* is too big to be hidden behind a palm tree.

This was not all I had on my mind as I drove to keep my appointment with Bill Thoman and the "physician from Peru." President Kennedy's Alliance for Progress had just been launched; the Bay of Pigs was a very recent memory, and Castro was at the height of his popularity in Latin America; the entire Southern Hemisphere was dangerously restless. Strikes and riots were hitting Bolivia, Brazil, Guiana, and Argentina with monotonous regularity—"Communist inspired," it was said, but actually the products of genuine misery, long ignored by the governments in control, and by our own as well. Everywhere the people of Latin America were demanding a change, any change. And why not? If existing conditions assured the average citizen of only thirty years of life, wouldn't any change from the *status quo* be an improvement? On this program of "any change is better than none," left-wing-oriented candidates were everywhere rising from the ruins created by loss of pride and lack of hope. We in the United States were finally beginning to recognize that the "Latin problem" was our problem.

The old Washington Hotel, home of the Aviation Club, came into sight, and beyond it, the White House; as always, I was reassured by its sheer physical presence. Today I needed all the confidence, all the bolstering my country's symbols of freedom could give me. I sensed that the "physician from Peru" would have questions to ask of me and—through me—of HOPE. I knew little of Peru and the attitude of Peruvians, and wondered in advance how I might answer questions—possibly suspicious—about a Project designed to give medical aid freely with only one proviso: it must be freely received.

I needn't have plagued myself with such doubts. From the first moment of Bill's introduction of Dr. Fernando Cabieses— or Cabby, as he quickly asked me to call him—we were *simpático,* a quality I came to value highly in the months to come. His face was warm and friendly, his eyes a bright, clear blue, and when he spoke of the needs of his country there were a strength and a determination in his attitude that inspired instant confidence. There was no fencing in his conversation, spoken in almost perfect English learned in studying medicine for seven years in this country. He had chosen, however, to return to work among his own people—unlike so many of his colleagues who had remained to practice here.

"Dr. Walsh," he began, "Bill tells me that you have a Project that may help the people of my country. From what I have heard and read, we need it. If you are willing to consider working in Peru, let us talk. If not, I would be grateful if you would tell me now."

This was more than impressive as an opener. It had a directness I was not accustomed to in my previous dealings with the representatives of many foreign countries.

"I'll listen," was my reply.

"Good enough," he said.

"My friends call me Cabby, and if we are going to work together—which I am going to try to convince you we should —you will be my *amigo.*" From time to time he lapsed into a Spanish phrase or word.

"In my country there is much misunderstanding of the North American, not only among the poor but even more so among the educated. For example, in my own profession of medicine there are almost four hundred Peruvians who have studied in the United States. Perhaps half of them choose to remember the good, and have a great love for your country. The rest confuse me; they hate the gringo, they hate the United States."

"Cabby," I asked, "does their success as physicians seem to make a difference in their feelings after they return home?"

"Of course," he replied. "Those who fail find a way to blame it on the training they received in the States. You taught them the wrong things. People were unkind to them. They need a whipping boy. They are no different from those politicians who blame all their failures on exploitation from the North. The fact that they have promised what they cannot possibly deliver makes no difference. The same is true of these doctors. They feel that because they have North American training the whole world will be theirs when they return home. Unfortunately, this attitude won't help our people live longer."

"I know that in Peru you have many well-trained physicians; but aren't the great majority of them concentrated in Lima, and doesn't this make it impossible for all of them to earn a decent living?" I asked.

"Yes," Cabby replied, "but that is only one problem. Outside of Lima there is little educational stimulus, but even in the capital medical education is hamstrung by student politics, the government, and squabbles among the doctors themselves. Even at the oldest medical school in this hemisphere we do not have proper training programs or enough nurses and other auxiliary medical personnel.

"We need help," he declared unabashedly, "and we need it now!"

Our conversation lasted for hours. It covered everything from the health of the Peruvians and the country's geography to the political pitfalls he felt lay immediately ahead. A violent anti-Communist, Cabby had nonetheless been criticized by the right as well as by the left. On the one hand he had resisted the attempt of the Communist-controlled student group at Lima's San Marcos University to take over the medical faculty, and had led in the formation of the "Cayatano Heredia," a new faculty of outstanding teachers free of Communist influence. On the other hand, his insistence upon the need for social reform, medical care for the indigent in the barrios surrounding Lima, and his arguments for spreading medical talent throughout Peru from Lima had incurred the wrath of the traditionalists. Fortunately, he was one of the most highly skilled neurosurgeons in South America, and his talent enabled him to survive the criticism.

Cabby's sense of charity endeared him to the underprivileged. His philosophy and ambition puzzled many. But he represented a rapidly growing group in Latin America who had adopted that old gringo adage: "Don't just stand there, do something!"

He had read of HOPE's efforts in Asia, and was convinced that we could accomplish two great objectives by working in Peru. One was to upgrade and modernize the approach to medical education; where an oligarchy persisted, the old refused to change, resisting and frustrating the young. The well trained, unless they were in a subspecialty such as his own neurosurgery, were held back. They had to go elsewhere for their training, for the experienced would not teach them for fear of losing control to upcoming competition. It was this attitude, he explained, that brought on student unrest and strikes. One could not give in to control by the students, but one must realize the cause of their unrest. He felt that if we could only demonstrate for a period of time in a school in his country our own proved philosophy that to teach is to progress and that each physician is made a better one by the students he trains, much could be gained.

His other objective was to provide medical care for the poor, who were receiving little or none, and thus show the people of Peru that the gringo was good.

I learned from Cabby that almost all doctors in Peru—and throughout Latin America—received some compensation from either the federal or municipal government, supposedly to enable them to donate part of their time to serving the poor. But this income is incredibly low; $100 to $150 a month for a man who has devoted half his life and a great deal of money to his education is ridiculous. Therefore, the physician must "moonlight" with wealthy private patients, leaving little free time for the poor. It is unfair to state that the Latin American physician lacks social consciousness—"lack of social awareness" might be a better term—but under the present system the competent organization and administration of a free clinic are quite beyond his scope. A corollary to this situation is the fear that the masses will realize that they are medically deprived by their own doctors—and they do. Then too, resentment of the gringo is aggravated by the so-called company or hacienda medical compounds. Here, employees of foreign companies or large local planters receive medical care from company-employed physicians. This is necessary and it is right, for it is a recognition that the human being is still the single most important economic unit around. However, to the thousands of destitute who are either unemployed or employed elsewhere at wages too low to provide for their families, it is like waving a red flag at a bull. There is nothing more inflammatory than to have a well-equipped, well-manned company hospital being forced to turn away a sick patient because the patient is not employed by the right company. Yet, if the doors were thrown open to all the hospital would be overrun.

Talk of these and other problems made the time pass so rapidly that it seemed we had hardly spent an hour together, yet when we took the time to look up, we found that the dining room had long since emptied. A seed had been planted that was to flower in the arid coastal desert of Peru only six months later.

Cabieses left to return to Lima as quickly as possible, after suggesting to me that if we would come to Peru, he felt that

[2]

Only a matter of weeks after Cabby's departure from Washington, the formal invitation did arrive from the Dean of the Faculty of Medicine at the University of Trujillo. Many words, both by letter and telephone, passed between us, and then the time came for me to visit Peru, meet with appropriate health officials in Lima, then journey to Trujillo, where I would participate in my first meeting with the faculty council.

It had been agreed that Cabby would act as overall chairman of the Peruvian HOPE Committee. Since, as a result of the feud at the University of San Marcos in Lima—between students and faculty, and the younger and older members of the faculty—Cabby and many of his colleagues had submitted their resignations to the university, and because we of HOPE were already so identified with the rebellious group, any opportunity for cooperation at San Marcos was eliminated.

Initially this caused little or no harm. The Minister of Health, Teddy Watson, recognized the need for a delaying action, and cooperated with both groups. In fact, we would be in a much better position to fulfill our purpose of encouraging the new medical school at Trujillo to adopt modern teaching methods than ever would have been possible if we had had to divide our staff to placate the entrenched faculty at San Marcos. Even more important, we would be working well to the north of Lima, helping to counteract the capital's exclusive influence, a development long needed.

I planned my first visit to the Land of the Incas for early December, 1961. I had been told the weather would be good; the *garúa*, that heavy mist that covers the entire coast throughout the summer, would have long since vanished. I would have the chance to see this land—really three countries in one—at an ideal time.

The Incas had called Peru "Land of the Four Quarters," but geography divides it into thirds—coastal desert, sierra, and jungle: three cultures, three climates, yet one people. The country I was to know best was the more than fourteen hundred miles of coastal desert, stretching from Chile in the South to the disputed boundary with Ecuador in the North. I had been told that there had been no rain along this particular stretch since 1923, and as I flew over, I believed it. Dotted periodically is an oasis of green here and there among the desert sands, irrigated by rivers or streams descending from the foothills of the Sierra, miles from the coast. Lima itself, watered by the Rimac River, flowers the year round. Yet, fully a third or more of the population live in this barren coastal area. While it produces some cotton, sugar, and to the north some oil, much of it is sand that covers the ruins of the pre-Columbian and even pre-Incan civilizations.

One of the most lucrative pastimes for unemployed Peruanos along this coast is grave robbing. Each night many Huágueros (as coastal dwellers are known) go into the mounds left by buried civilizations to recover the treasures of an ancient culture. The dryness of the coastal plain has preserved better than any tomb the textiles, pottery, and other artifacts of the Mochica, Nascan, and Paracas civilizations that are recovered in a perfectly preserved state, and sold. Some of these finds are over two thousand years old. The textiles, especially, are a wonder to behold, for the weaving technique of the pre-Inca inhabitants of Peru has never been duplicated. Historians tell us the Incas did all within their power to destroy every remnant of the cultures that preceded them so that only their own imprint would remain for the future.

The blandness of the desert is broken only by the coastal link of the Pan American Highway, which snakes through the desert. Occasionally, this road is interrupted by a major city like Arequipa, Peru's second largest city, in the South, or Trujillo, her third largest city, which lies almost a thousand miles to the north. The former is frequently called the Texas of Peru because of its great wealth and the independence of its citizenry. It is in Arequipa that the revolutions which have plagued Peru's history have so often begun.

The coastal highway, not quite wide enough for a large truck or bus and another vehicle to pass comfortably, is a kind of House of Horrors. The Peruvian driver shouts *"Estúpido camerone!"* at his adversary rather than give way, and he has been responsible for landscaping the highway with crosses and shrines, erected to commemorate the losers. Anyone who drives along this stretch of highway at less than sixty miles an hour—even in an ancient and occasionally "brakeless" *colectivo*—is held in contempt. The population explosion will never be a problem in this third of Peru—not while this highway exists.

The people of the coastal plain seem to be a happy lot, nonetheless. At least they dance the *marinera* night after night and are responsible for producing the famous *pisco,* an alcoholic beverage that has become renowned the world over, and is synonomous with Peru. To the uninitiated, *pisco* is hidden dynamite. It is a drink that, when disguised with lemon and egg white, seems as benign as mother's milk. Then suddenly a kind of amnesia settles on the victim. I remember the tale of an American businessman who recalled being with friends some ninety miles from Lima; then, two days later, he waked up in his hotel in New York. His companions told him that he had driven his own car to Lima, packed his bags, checked out of the hotel, made his air connection on schedule, and arrived in New York. There, he proceeded to his hotel and went to bed, rising to find that he had neglected only two things. One was to take off his clothes before going to bed; the other was fully to enclose his neckties in his suitcase. He has not imbibed since.

My arrival in Lima was without incident, and at once I was taken over by Cabby, who had arranged to accompany me on the drive to Trujillo. Several times along the way my foot would press against an imaginary brake as our driver negotiated a curve at seventy miles an hour, two thousand feet above the sea, but Cabby only smiled broadly, and never once stopped talking.

"Yes, Bill, we have the agreement of the Minister of Health and the blessing of our President Prado, who wants to meet you while you are here so that he can give you his personal assurance of cooperation and can sign the *convento* before you leave. Everything you have requested has been agreed upon."

It was over an hour before we arrived at a small coastal town where Cabby told the driver to stop. It was time to eat.

"First, Bill, we must show you some Peruvian history; we'll make a Peruano out of you before you know it. This village is very important in our history. Simón Bolívar lived here in Huachi for a time, and he proclaimed the independence of Peru from that very balcony." He pointed to an unimposing and restored wooden balustrade two stories above the street; the pride in his voice gave the place unexpected luster. The rest of the town was a carbon copy of any Hollywood producer's idea of a small South American town. The highway ran through the center, and was bordered by two nondescript rows of buildings. Some had two stories, some only one; a few were brick, but most were either adobe or a mixture of cane, mud, and tin. The sturdiest building in town was the cathedral, which seemed to have withstood the elements for centuries, though it was far from the oldest in Peru. I noticed a great many dogs and cats and saw that the walls carried the same slogan in different colors: *Cuba sí, Yanqui no.* An election campaign was in progress, and one feature of the local "democracy" is the understanding that the supporter of each candidate may write slogans anywhere. This town obviously belonged to Haya de la Torre, the left-wing candidate for President, and was so poor it was easy to see why the extreme left flourishes alongside misery and despair.

We walked down the sleepy, dusty street until we found a rather alarming little restaurant. As we entered, I asked Cabby, "Is this place all right?"

"Sure, Bill, sure," he answered. "Just don't drink the water. The driver says it's the best restaurant between here and Trujillo. Besides, it's this or nothing until tonight. I'm going to introduce you to real Peruvian food. Don't worry; it will be so hot no bacteria could live in it anyway."

"I hope you're right," I replied as I looked around the "best restaurant between here and Trujillo." Flies descended on the filthy tables in swarms. The floor was wooden and muddy; the walls were painted a sick green. The proprietor leaned over a counter in the back, and beyond him another room was hidden by a soiled curtain. From the odors I assumed that it must be the kitchen.

The moment we were seated he shuffled slowly toward us and said, "Buenos días, señores," paused briefly, then questioned, "Cerveza?"

Cabby laughed. "See, Bill, he already knows you are a gringo, and wants to serve you beer. All gringos like Peruvian beer." Cabby answered him, "Sí, dos cervezas—grandes," and then in rapid Spanish went on to order our lunch.

During lunch we discussed the problems of the current

political campaign and its three candidates: Haya de la Torre, representing the extreme left; Fernando Belaunde Terry, center or slightly left of center; and a former President, General Odria, extreme right. As Cabby talked, it was plain that he was a Belaundista who passionately feared a Haya victory. Haya had promised the people a change overnight, something that simply was not possible. Cabby was critical of the American government's support of Haya. Our Embassy was accused of interfering in the election, and it was becoming impossible to convince the people that Haya was not being backed by us. Cabby felt this was a serious error, and he went on to say that the military forces of Peru would never tolerate the election of Haya de la Torre. This was the first inkling I had that HOPE might once again be caught in the middle of a local political fight.

It was here, too, that I realized to what an extent we in North America had permitted the Communists and the extreme left to monopolize and merchandise the word and atmosphere of "change" as something that could be brought about only by their system. No matter what your politics might be, if you demonstrated a sincere desire to help the poor and underprivileged, the masses automatically concluded you must be a Red.

Cabby, Belaunde, and others like them were members of the growing middle class who wanted to bring change, but without military dictatorship or bloody revolution. A social revolution, yes, but no armed conflict. Cabby explained over and over again that we must reach the people, let them know that tomorrow would be better than their hopeless yesterday. This is why he wanted to bring the symbol of HOPE to Trujillo, not only as a means of improving medical education and increasing the numbers of trained medical manpower but also to demonstrate to the people that the Yanqui and his system could bring about some of the change for which they had been waiting so long. The gringo must become identified with progress, not *status quo* or colonialism. HOPE could, he said, be a preview of progress throughout his nation and the continent as well.

This discussion lasted through two *grandes cervezas,* and then came that Peruvian lunch. We began with *ceviche,* a dish of marinated raw corvina, Peru's most tasty fish. It was riddled with raw onions and spotted with pieces of the *aji,* a hot orange pepper. After the first mouthful, I knew why no bacteria could survive it: amoebas would most assuredly be consumed by it rather than the reverse. However, after the first shock, I found it excellent, and it became a daily delight for me after that. It was followed by *anticuchos,* a shish kebab of Peru. Beef hearts are roasted over hot coals or eucalyptus embers, and served on a wooden stick. They were delicious. After this came the standard fried corvina and dessert. The restaurant I had entered so doubtfully had provided us with a menu to rival that of the Four Seasons. Even better, the entire meal for two cost us less than a dollar and a half.

Contented and well fed, we resumed our drive toward Trujillo. Cabby felt I had become at least part Peruvian, and I, in turn, knew that my *amigo* had given me both his trust and a briefing no one else could have provided.

After some four hours a quite unbelievable odor descended upon us. The driver automatically closed his windows, and Cabby said calmly, "Close your windows, Bill; we are about ten miles from Chimbote, and it gets worse from here on in."

Chimbote was a sight and smell I shall never forget. It was also an object lesson in the problems we were soon to face. This huge settlement was called by many the "Pittsburgh of Peru," because it had almost overnight become the industrial center of the country. The stench was not that of steel and coke, however, but rather that of scorching and steaming fish. It penetrates everything for miles around, and sticks to clothes until they are cleaned. The town itself is one massive *barriada,* housing over one hundred thousand people, having mushroomed from only five thousand some six years before as factories moved in to process the millions of fish. The fish are *anchovetas,* which resemble sardines and grow up to four inches long. They are sucked up into fishing boats by giant hoses and are then immediately taken to the factories by truck, and are dumped into a well. From the well they pass to a cooker, then successively through a sieve, press, rotating oven, and grinder. Finally they wind up as dried, pulverized fish meal, and are put in sacks for export. This has overnight become Peru's largest export industry. Pigs and chickens throughout the world are growing fat on the *anchovetas* from these coastal waters.

But along with all this rapid growth and full employment, overcrowding, disease, and misery came to Chimbote. The cries for land reform and low-cost housing, higher wages and medical care precipitated violence and political unrest. The all too familiar signs of agitation and lack of understanding were advertised everywhere across tin and cane walls: *Comunismo sí. Yanqui, go home.*

"You see, Bill," Cabby said, "you Norteamericanos are blamed for everything, even where there is prosperity. This industry has grown so fast that housing has been impossible, sewage disposal worse, and those sophisticated benefits of your society, like workmen's compensation and health insurance, are not available. There are not enough doctors and nurses in all northern Peru to bring adequate medical care to Chimbote. This is why we need you so badly. Trujillo is only one hour from here. If we can make it a medical center for the North, it will be a great step forward. The doctors and dentists will stop moving to Lima, and some beginning of orderly community planning can take place. Time is growing short. And, my friend, the people will not wait much longer."

We drove on in silence, until suddenly the driver said with

unmistakable pride, "When we come around the next turn, you will see my city of Trujillo in the valley."

Trujillo, the county seat of Libertad Department, lay inland from the sea. The straight line of the coast took a sharp bend, and you could see the surf breaking on the shore for miles, until it disappeared over the horizon. As we came to the foot of the hill, we found ourselves in a city of some forty thousand people. It was still a classical colonial city in the older section, many of the homes with balustrades above the streets. There was also a "downtown" section with a bank and modern stores, yet the town had not lost its Old World flavor. It was built around the usual Spanish plaza, with its own local hero astride a steel horse right in its center. The park was filled with people strolling, talking, or just enjoying the sun. Barefoot shoeshine boys, later to prove irresistible to our personnel, were everywhere. It was busy and yet relaxed; no one seemed to be hurrying. On one side of the plaza was the huge cathedral of Trujillo, one of the oldest in the country, and the parish church of Archbishop Pérez Silva. As we drove around the square we stopped before the Turista Hotel, one of a chain of government-operated hostels, our home for the next few days. It was painted a pale pink, and its simulated old Spanish architecture complemented the plaza and its flowers. Bellboys in handsome white uniforms ran to help with the baggage. It was odd to find such a city in the middle of the coastal desert, yet it was the third largest in Peru, and one of its oldest cultural centers. The University of Trujillo was well known throughout the land.

It was in the lobby of the hotel that I first met two people whose friendship would prove to be vital to our success in Peru. One was Dr. Jorge de Vinatea Collins, who was then professor of anatomy at the medical school, and the second was Pío Roselle, Director of the Peruvian–North American Cultural Society.

Dr. Vinatea, professor of anatomy and volunteer coordinator

of Project HOPE, was a tall, gangling man who gave us a
somewhat puzzled look over his black-rimmed glasses as he
extended his hand in greeting. Certainly no Clark Gable, he
frequently described himself as "the ugliest man in Trujillo."
Born in Arequipa thirty-eight years ago, he had moved to
Trujillo when the new school opened in 1958. One of our
volunteers, Dr. Eldon Ellis, a surgeon from San Francisco,
later said that "Jorge was one of the few men in Trujillo who
could think like a Peruvian and a North American at the same
time."

Jorge Vinatea had gone to San Marcos Medical School in
Lima, where he had become friends with Cabby. Following
graduation and some training in Peru, Jorge had taken his
graduate training in obstetrics and gynecology at a hospital in
Akron, Ohio. His experience there was an unhappy one, and he
will rarely discuss it; but when he does, it is with sufficient
bitterness to make one wonder why he is still fond of the
gringos. Upon his return to Peru, he worked first in an Obrero
(workers') hospital and later as physician with an American-
owned mining concern. In 1958 he was appointed professor of
anatomy at the new medical school in Trujillo.

He told me that when Cabby approached him about the
Hope's coming to Trujillo, he immediately recognized it as a
tremendous opportunity, especially for the development of the
new medical school. When it was suggested, however, that he
coordinate the program at the Trujillo end, he had mixed
emotions. He frankly felt it was a gamble. But while recogniz-
ing that he would probably be unpopular with the students
and physicians, already resentful of the Norteamericano, he
finally concluded that if the program were successful, both the
school and his people would benefit. He also knew that his
own future would be laid on the line. Failure of the HOPE
mission would probably result in his dismissal from the faculty.
This Peruano, who could also think like a Yanqui, who could

forget his bitter experience in the States, took the chance, and
the die was cast. I don't believe that anyone else in Trujillo
could have equaled his accomplishment, nor have done more
to make our mission a success.

Next to greet us was Pío Roselle, who, together with his
wife, Tenny, was to be a part of Hope throughout the year
that followed. He was a constantly smiling, handsome Tru-
jillano who served us as a jack-of-all-trades, helping with
whatever problem arose, arranging recreation for the staff, and,
above all, making the finest *pisco* sours in all Peru. On count-
less occasions it was Pío who rescued us from our frustrations.
Both of Pío's sons were later invited to the United States as
guests of families of physicians who had served in Trujillo; this
was the kind of friend he was to become.

The preliminaries concluded, we proceeded to the medical
school for a meeting with the dean, some members of his
faculty, and the coordinating committee selected by them. The
school itself was a pleasant surprise. It was a two-story white
building, occupying a square block, the latest addition to the
university, and quite modern. There was a border of flowers
around it, and it was protected by an iron fence some forty
feet from the windows of the building; it was frequently
suggested this was more a precaution against violent student
strikes than against thievery.

Once in the building, we were escorted to the board room,
where a small group of men awaited us. As we came into the
room, they all rose, but I could not help noticing that only one
smiled in greeting. This was Percy Falcon, head of the Department of Pathology. The faces of the rest of the group wore
expressions varying from something less than restrained enthusiasm to outright hostility.

Dean Olguin welcomed us on behalf of the group. He spoke
in halting English, but I was soon to find that when he or the
group wished to conceal their thoughts they would lapse into

rapid Spanish. The meeting progressed well; without denying
their need of our help, the committee made clear their concern
that we might interfere in their private practice. As I listened,
I looked at each of the men and wondered which would be our
friends. What about Dr. Acuña, Professor of Surgery at Belén
Hospital, the hospital affiliated with the medical school? He
was an oligarch in medical circles, and no one at Belén was
permitted to perform any surgery until Dr. Acuña's own
schedule was completed. Skilled, proud, and quizzical, he
looked as if he could be difficult. And why not? Here we were
preparing to invade his domain at someone else's invitation.

There was Alejandro Ulloa, an internist about my own age.
Trained in the United States, married to an American girl, he
was the proud possessor of a bright blue Cadillac, which
seemed out of place in the quaint, narrow streets of Trujillo.
He was slight of build and wore a cocksure smile. I had heard
him referred to as a *gringoya* by some of his envious colleagues, a term used to describe those Latins who would like
to be North Americans. No, it is not complimentary. Yet all
knew his competence, and we later found him to be a true
friend. Now there seemed to be an air of challenge in his
attitude.

Another in the gathering caught my eye. Dr. Alvaro Canales,
a slender, dapper-looking chap, with a thin moustache. His
eyes were bright and his movements rapid. He was responsible
for most of the orthopedics in Trujillo, although primarily self-
trained. He also represented the Trujillanos in the Medical
Federation of Peru, the Peruvian version of the AMA. It was
he who revealed to us the federation's concern that we might
threaten the private practice of Peruvian physicians. We knew
that the federation had approved the invitation to HOPE with
reluctance, and Canales wanted to report to Lima our further
reassurance on this score.

On the whole, the meeting was successful and the reaction

of the faculty good. We knew that Dr. Vinatea and Dr. Falcon would be on our side and that the others would work with us on a wait-and-see basis. We knew, too, that no matter what we told them, they had no real conception of the size of the undertaking to which they were committing themselves. No one ever does.

Following our meeting we all went out to the beach to Morilla's for lunch. This was Trujillo's finest restaurant, and was to become the favorite of all our staff, its stone floors and salt-sprayed windows a welcome refuge from the ship. The proprietor, a generously proportioned Peruvian who was most proud of his English, always had a blackboard standing in the back of the room with American slogans chalked on it, anything from *Go, you Brooklyn Dodgers* (a little dated) to a homely idiom or traditional proverb. Each day the words would change, but something was always there.

In this atmosphere of pounding breakers and warming *Pisco* sours, a spirit of agreement and cooperation was formed. Our reconnaissance mission to Trujillo had been a success. We decided to defer other meetings with the citizens of the community, and so headed back to Lima, this time by air. Cabby and I both slept with the peace of mind that comes with a job well done.

[3]

After my return to Washington, planning began at a furious pace. Cabby and I had tentatively agreed upon a late spring sailing date for the *Hope* and drugs, food, supplies and equipment had to be obtained. There was every indication that many of the staff that had been with us in the Far East would return, but no one knew how many replacements must be recruited. Money, as always, was still a problem. Nevertheless, we at this end and Cabby at the other went forward with all possible speed.

Volunteer applications poured in by the hundreds, and our staff was selected. Dorothy Aeschliman, Ann Roden, and Nancy Campion, all veterans of our first voyage, took time out from temporary jobs to interview and select staff nurses and secretaries. Gloria Aguilera, Pris Strong, and a host of others talked about the *Hope* to anyone who would listen. Herb Bloom organized the physicians and dentists of Detroit into an active chapter that promptly "Hoped" all over Michigan. Not content with this, Herb also helped set up a citizens' committee in Detroit, and these community chapters later spread to every county in Michigan. He then convinced the American Dental Association to take an active and continuing part in our program.

On the West Coast, Marty Kohn, a veteran of our Saigon mission, spread the word, assisted by some forty colleagues in the San Francisco area. In Los Angeles, Henry Bodner, urologist and Indonesian veteran, told our story at every university hospital, and flooded us with volunteers. All these and many others took on the extra chores of updating our equipment lists, buttonholing friends and business acquaintances in an effort to get us sailing on schedule.

Norm Hoover, orthopedist at the Mayo Clinic, together with Al Miller, a colleague from Cleveland, concentrated on keeping the Saigon Rehabilitation Center staffed and supplied. Both were shortly to return there to continue the work that would ultimately bring to over twenty-eight hundred crippled children in that war-torn land the hope of walking again.

The spirit of *Hope* was never stronger; the determination of its team never greater. We moved heaven and earth to keep on schedule. Then, just as we felt that we might make it, a strike hit the West Coast shipping industry. Now we knew that a delay was unavoidable.

We have often referred in the past to our "guardian angel," and he seemed to be still hovering above us. Our negotiations with the government for funds to subsidize our operating differential had been lagging, yet we needed far more repair work on the ship than originally anticipated. Our teams had been selected to leave in March and our permanent staff was completed, but there was no chance of sailing before the other problems were solved. As always, however, the story of HOPE is people, and our wonderful people came to the rescue. Some nurses had already quit their previous positions and proceeded to the West Coast to await sailing; unemployed, they were our responsibility. Yet their spirit and devotion were such that not one turned to us for help, nor did we lose a single volunteer. HOPE alumni and alumnae on the coast helped some of them find temporary employment; others worked in department stores when nothing else was available. Not one complained. Their only question to Washington was one we were hourly asking ourselves: "When do we sail?"

Cabby and I agreed that rather than lose our first team of

rotating doctors we would send them down ahead of the ship. Cabby assured me he would work out a plan to use their services, and I was to go ahead as scheduled. HOPE was to arrive in Peru without a ship, but with a group of some twenty-two physicians along with four of our nurses, all but one veterans of the first voyage, in an effort to make up for lost time before the ship arrived. The girls would have the opportunity to plan the nursing program, select the students, and get a feel of the situation. We chose Nancy Campion, from Waterbury, Connecticut; Mary Damuth, from Utica, New York; Gloria Aguilera, from Pueblo, Colorado (the only one of the group who spoke good Spanish); and LaVerne Fakkema, a public health nurse from San Francisco, California. LaVerne was the only newcomer, but we wanted her slant on public health problems. We added Priscilla Strong, our chief nurse anesthetist from Pittsfield, Massachusetts, in the event our surgeons should need her.

Later, Cabby related to me an incident that involved Nancy Campion and Mary Damuth. Nancy is a daily communicant in the Catholic Church, a woman of saintly virtue, beautiful voice, and full heart. Mary is one of our most compassionate pediatric nurses, with a tenderness so encompassing we used her on our first HOPE Christmas card, holding a sick Indonesian child.

These two women were given the task of trying to establish rapport with Señora Malpartida, the Director of Nursing in Peru. Señora Malpartida, a powerful person in the Ministry of Health, rules nursing in Peru with an iron hand. Well educated, she is surrounded by a small team of nurses, all of whom have had college-level nurses' training in the United States. They had been making every effort to elevate the level of nurses' training in Peru and to endow it with the proper professional respect. By dint of their efforts, they felt much progress had been made; now they were suddenly to be visited by advance "experts" from HOPE.

We were unaware that Señora Malpartida's department had not been fully consulted by Cabby, and he in turn thought someone else had done the briefing. Nancy and Mary, anticipating a warm welcome, were instead met with resentment— the source of which was a mystery to them. One rebuff followed another, and finally, as Nancy put it, "We'd had it. We were determined that we would develop a nursing and nursing auxiliary program despite them." She reasoned, "After all, we're here to help these people, and whether they like it or not, we'll help them."

It is quite true that Peru was dreadfully short of nurses, and the physicians there were daily hampered by lack of assistants. Nancy and Mary were simply attempting to describe our ideas and make certain that students who gave their time to HOPE would receive some credit. The hospitals outside Lima were in serious need of more trained womanpower. HOPE's basic mission anywhere is for a year, and if our skills are not taken advantage of, then the people of the host nation are not using all our facilities to help themselves. Acceptance of our training programs is always a prime requirement in any mission that we undertake.

Nancy and Mary, taking the bull by the horns, went out and had some calling cards printed with their names inscribed in bold type. Taking advantage of their growing knowledge of Spanish, they identified themselves as representing (in capital letters) ESPERANZA, the Spanish word for "HOPE." From that time onward, they were accepted wherever they went, particularly by officials of the government and the physicians in Lima.

Cabby laughs whenever he tells anyone: "To this day I don't believe that Nancy and Mary ever realized that at that time 'Esperanza' was the name of one of the fanciest bordellos in Lima. It was frequented only by the best people, so you can imagine the shock when these two gringas presented their cards. It was even more of a shock when those they visited found them to be on legitimate business." Then he adds: "I have never had the courage to tell them. But at least they had the opportunity to see all the right people."

Just at the time our two nurses were making reputations for themselves in Lima, the first group of rotators arrived ("rotators" being our name for the series of teams that replace one another during a mission). Cabby had done his job well, and he and one of our advance administrative representatives, Stacy Lloyd, had obtained a house in suburban San Isidro, known forever after as "Casa Hope." This was provided as a courtesy by the Lima HOPE Committee organized by Cabby. It was big enough for about half the group, the remainder staying for the night at a hotel in town.

It was a kind of halfway house, a stopoff between Lima and other cities where we were working, and Stacy had equipped it in Sears, Roebuck style from top to bottom, with bunk beds, four to a room, and other furnishings to match. Along with the house came Ester, the housekeeper, and few of our rotators or nurses will forget her efforts to accommodate twelve to fourteen gringos at a time, without ever learning one word of English. She did learn American ways, and always had the refrigerator bulging with beer, cheese, and cold cuts.

The night after our arrival, Stacy had arranged for a reception at Casa Hope so that we could meet with as many Peruvian physicians as possible. It was apparent from the spread, that among Stacy's other attributes was a voracious appetite. A tall, handsome, quiet lad, he had been with us in Vietnam, and was later to leave us for the State Department. The evening went beautifully, and it was apparent that, ship or no ship, we were welcome in Peru.

Among those who joined us at the reception were Julian Smith, a good friend of Cabieses, and a representative of Cerra del Pasco Mining Company. Another was Dr. Arturo Vassi, an old school friend of Cabby's, now charged with the responsibility of revitalizing several Obrero hospitals in the remote areas of the country. These were the hospitals established to provide medical care for the laboring class or blue-collar workers. Though built under government sponsorship, Obrero hospitals were supported actively by the private medical community. Many private physicians were retained on a part-time basis, but there was considerable difficulty in getting the better ones to work far away from home. Vassi had done an excellent job reorganizing such a hospital south of Lima, and was about to pay the price of his success. He had been commissioned to do the same job for the Obrero hospital in Oroya, home of Cerra del Pasco. This was why the three of them had backed me into a corner. Cabby opened: "Bill, my friend, this is what we have planned for your doctors and nurses until your ship gets here. Arturo needs them in Oroya; Mr. Smith's company owns the railroad, and will transport you there. We will provide housing, food, and anything you want. Just help us in that hospital."

"Just a moment," I replied, "what about Trujillo? Our first obligation is to them."

"I know," said Cabby, "but they cannot afford to house such a large group and are willing to wait for the ship."

At this point, Arturo Vassi interrupted in his high, husky voice that always sounded as if he were just recovering from laryngitis. "Besides, I have all the money you want." His eyes sparkled with enthusiasm. "There is much to be done in Oroya; they have ten doctors, a large broken-down hospital, and no one knows where to begin. If you find equipment is needed, just order it. We will buy it. This is a great opportunity for us. Maybe you will like it so much you will stay the whole year in Oroya."

Julian Smith added that it would do no harm to let the area see that Americans were concerned with something other than mining company affairs. His firm, Cerra del Pasco, had its own

[4]

During those April and early May days, while our advance units were endeavoring to bring HOPE to Oroya and lay a foundation in Trujillo, we were doing our best to get the ship out of California. The shipping strike had tied up everything on the West Coast for weeks, and not until the President invoked the Taft-Hartley Act were we able to hire a crew. The Grace Line, our country's most experienced shipper to the West Coast of South America, had agreed to operate the vessel. Thank the Lord they did. Their people proved invaluable, and their knowledge of the coastline alone saved the Foundation several hundred thousands of dollars.

Finally, on May 9, 1962, Captain Elijah Howe piloted our gracious lady under the Golden Gate Bridge and headed south. The twelve days at sea were, as on the previous mission, all work and no play; the staff had to police the hospital areas. Dorothy Aeschliman, who had taken over as chief nurse, together with many veterans of our Far East cruise and a cadre of new and enthusiastic Hopies, directed the cleanup from morning till night. Four physician volunteers sailed with the permanent staff, and all "turned to" under Dorothy's stern commands.

It was described by a medical writer for a Cleveland newspaper as

no pleasure cruise. . . . Hospital people, usually seen in starched white, and gravely professional, are barefoot, in sandals and work clothes. They ply mops and brooms. They are scrubbing and scouring to prepare the hospital of this ship for an open house at Lima, and for the reception of patients at Salaverry, port of Trujillo, soon afterwards. Some of the doctors have stripped to the waist. In the patient wards where beds are fixed to walls or stanchions, some of the nurses lie down in order to wash the underparts. Others climb on the beds to wash their supports or the walls alongside them.

The workday began immediately after breakfast, and lasted as long as necessary. The department heads bore the responsibility, each for his own, and kept their staffs working through the day and sometimes after dinner on wall-washing or floor-mopping "parties."

The work schedule was broken into periodically by an educational program arranged by the Reverend Frederic J. Green, S.J., assistant pastor of Sagrario Parish in Tacna, Peru. He had been home on sick leave, and asked if he could "work" his way back to Peru so that the money thus saved could be used for the poor of his parish. We were delighted to have him just as a passenger, and hoped that he would rest. He was not long recovered from a severe bout of infectious hepatitis, and was still very weak and easily fatigued.

Nevertheless, from the second day out until our arrival he directed an education program, teaching many classes himself. He had five volunteer faculty members, all from our own staff: Anita Soto, a refugee teacher from the University of Oriente, Santiago, Cuba, now a lab technician on the *Hope;* the Reverend David Edmunds of San Antonio, Texas, Protestant chaplain; the Reverend John Magner, S.J., Catholic chaplain; Miss Vivian Crosswhite of Urbana, Ohio, physical therapist; and Miss Velma Lutz of Trotwood, Ohio, a nurse.

Spanish language classes were part of the program, but it was Father Green's lectures in the evening that the staff found most informative. He told them about the people, 10 percent white, 30 percent mestizo, and 60 percent pure Indian. He described the Peru we were going to help, not the travelogue country of mountains and stone temples. "In many areas," he said, "there is no plumbing and little water. People may live a lifetime without a bath. . . . Because of a famine in recent years and the difficulty of grubbing a living from the barren, treeless altiplano, a good many Indians are seeking better wages in the coastal cities, only to increase the size of the slums, which already present tremendous health problems. Here there may be only one water tap for five thousand persons living in abode houses. Human excrement and garbage pile up in the open because there is no method of disposing of it."

About Communism, Father Green said: "The Indians are a taciturn and melancholy people who have been in servitude for so many centuries that few people thought Communism would make any impression upon them. However, with the promise of change, the Communists are giving the Indians a ray of hope, and some of them are rallying to that side.

"Avoid political discussion if possible," he advised. "The quiet and effective work that you will do to teach and help the sick will be the best answer to whatever the Communists may say. Any attack on such work will do them more harm than good."

The *Hope* arrived in Lima on a sunny morning, May the twenty-first, and was visited with flattering promptness by the President of Peru and other dignitaries. President Prado, who was to be incarcerated by a military junta a couple of months later, was accompanied by the leaders of the armed forces, who seemed to be impressed by the size and facilities of the vessel, and realized for the first time the potential of its impact. This was to stand us in good stead later, but at the moment the most important result of this good impression was receiving final clearance to use our "ham" radio set.

We were already aware of the rumblings of a not too distant revolution, and wanted to be certain that Washington head-quarters could remain in communication with our units at La Oroya, the American Embassy in Lima, and the ship in Tru-jillo. Peruvian telephones being what they are, our only certain means of communication would be this gift from Hallicrafters and the "ham" operators of Peru. To demonstrate our need for the radio set, we called Gloria Aguilar in La Oroya, intending to hook her up with Craig Leman in Trujillo so that she could make the expected request for drugs or personnel. But a message now as famous to HOPE as the first by Morse went over the air: Gloria asked Dottie Aeschliman to send a "strap-less bra" via the next rotation of nurses. Tact prevents us from revealing the size, although it was likely recorded by some six thousand hams in various parts of the globe. In any case, we had proved both the innocence and necessity of the communi-cations setup. Permission was granted.

Welcoming festivities were soon over, and the *Hope* headed north for Trujillo. Within two days she nosed behind the breakwater to give the staff its first view of Salaverry, or Salaverry-by-the-Sea, as this Godforsaken port was ironically dubbed on the spot by Arnie Smoller, a young general practitioner and veteran of our first voyage. Arnie was also responsible for christening the bleak mountain of sand that rose behind Salaverry "The Poor Man's Rock of Gibraltar."

Captain Howe and other Grace Line personnel had pre-dicted all along that we would be unable to dock at Salaverry's rickety wooden pier, and as we felt the swell of the tide we realized they had been right. The Grace Line had already made plans to build a pontoon dock in order to bypass the pier, but even after it was ready, the *Hope* would have to anchor in the harbor about a hundred yards from shore, right in the midst of the busy harbor traffic. Salaverry is a sugar and molasses port, and lighters endlessly hauled cargo to and from freighters lying offshore. Until we got our own pontoon dock, patients and staff alike would have to make the ship-to-shore trip by launch and by foot, traversing some quarter of a mile of rotting planking.

Capping these initial disappointments was the less than enthusiastic welcome we received. Despite the fact that the *Hope* was probably the largest vessel ever to have put into Salaverry's harbor, only a dozen or so people and a sick-looking cow lined the shoreline. One of our greeters held a placard, and we read through binoculars: BEWARE OF THE YAN-KEE WARMONGERS. NOW THEY COME SHROUDED IN WHITE LIKE A DOVE OF PEACE. BEWARE!

But by this time we could spot a cloud of dust moving rapidly up the highway. Our official welcoming committee was on the way, and immediately following its arrival there was a reception on board the ship. The guests were brought to us by two of the dirtiest but happiest launches I have ever seen, the *Rosita* and the *Salaverry Queen*. The *Rosita* was presided over by a "captain" who must have weighed in at three hundred pounds. He was always smiling and—unfailingly—on duty twenty-four hours a day. We soon came to regard the *Rosita* as particularly ours. Her special feature, along with her massive captain, was a molasses- and dirt-caked little mongrel who made up in noise what he lacked in size. Day and night, he stood rigidly at the bow and barked his shrill greetings to all who boarded the launch. For reasons never disclosed, he was called Othello. Despite his name, his was a happy life, un-touched by tragedy, and his busy days left no time for Desdemona. Othello and the *Rosita* were never to miss a trip throughout the year. Every two minutes they would make their way to the ship with a cargo of misery and return to the shore with a cargo of hope.

Another character who entered our lives that day was to become a legend—a monster of a man, with a camera. He quickly became known as "Flash Gordo," for he snapped pictures more rapidly than a submachine gun fires bullets. I doubt that any of us ever heard him speak a word other than "ten soles" as he thrust out a batch of photographs. His advance intelligence was phenomenal. He knew before anyone else of every impending reception and official visitor; interesting cases, aboard or ashore, were known to him at once. He never stopped smiling, never angered a soul, and if he was not immediately spotted at appropriate occasions, all worried lest he had fallen ill. I feel certain he retired following our departure.

On the morning following the official reception, our staff on the ship was to be taken into Trujillo to see what our advance man, Craig Leman, who had already spent two months in the city, had been able to accomplish. Craig, a surgeon from Corvallis, Oregon, had already overstayed his rotation, but duty and obligation are his middle names. Buses had been arranged for, and would run the route between ship and town at thirty-minute intervals. This was but one of the many supporting contributions made by the townspeople of Trujillo.

Archie Golden, our staff pediatrician from New York City, described the first trip to Trujillo as an extraordinary experience:

The busses were about thirty years old, built to hold twenty or less people. More than thirty Hopies crowded into each one, and the only air inside was the result of the respirations of the passengers. The driver, Pepe, spoke no English but more than enough Spanish to coax his motor into starting. Then off we went in a cloud of sand and dust, our starched whites already a grim Trujillo brown. All of us were in wonderful spirit for we felt it was the real beginning of a great adventure. As we rattled down the road towards Trujillo, the contrasts of the community were apparent. A modern sports car or a new Mercedes would speed by, sending up clouds of dust into the faces of the miserably clad people walking the road. Here and there a farmer would be leading a lazy burro, carrying an

impossible load on his back. By the side of the road was an
overturned truck with what seemed hundreds of people attempting to relocate the load, which had tilted her over. Just as
we passed the little adobe village of Moche on our right, the
radiator of the bus let go with a roar of steam, and we ground
to a halt. Pepe turned with a smile and a gesture which
signified that we should not worry. He reached beneath his
seat for a green banana, an item without which we later
learned he never traveled. Under the front of the bus he went
and with a thrust stuffed the banana into the leaking radiator,
returned to his seat, and started his engine. To the amazement
of us all, the bus resumed her reasonably normal behavior.

As the bus entered the city proper, after passing the ruined
Chimu city of Chan-Chan, no smiles answered our own. Why?
The community obviously knew who we were. Our advance
unit had been among them almost two months. The students
had been at work. Yet *Comunismo si, Yanqui no* and *Yanqui,
go home* were still scrawled on almost every available wall.

The ability of an efficient organized minority to intimidate
or at the very least create uncertainty in the mind of an entire
city was apparent. Certainly there was no evidence of enthusiasm.

The Hopies, while shaken by this, became only more determined to put HOPE to work. We were a grim group until at
last, at Belén Hospital, we saw the sign *Programa HOPE*
painted in large white letters over the entrance to the outpatient clinics.

Jorge de Vinatea, smiling nervously and obviously under
tension, led the delegation to meet and guide us through the
hospital. Percy Falcon was warm in his greeting; the others
were retiring. Dr. Alfredo Acuña, strong man of the group,
openly showed his displeasure. As he explained later: "When
you North Americans first came, we did not trust you. The
gringos did not often come to Trujillo, and we frankly have
never liked them here. We were prepared to dislike you."

As professor of male surgery and senior member of the hospital staff, Acuña ran his department with an iron hand and was both feared and respected. Technically an excellent surgeon, he worked under impossible conditions. The inability of provincial hospitals to extract funds from Lima is well known, and Belén Hospital was no exception. We were soon to learn that they did the best they could; but, unfortunately, resentment of Lima frequently interfered with the hospital's ability to solve its problems. Peruvians are a proud people; Trujillanos are among the proudest of Peruvians.

As we were guided through the hospital wards and laboratories, we found much to be done. The shortage of trained nurses and technicians placed added burdens upon the physicians. No autoclaves were in operation, and old-fashioned wet sterilization methods were used in surgery. In wet sterilization, no pressure is used, and instruments and materials might just as well be run through a washing machine. In addition, the process is so long that an emergency appendectomy case, for instance, is subject to the same delay as a long-scheduled operation. The resulting postoperative infection rate is, therefore, astronomical. The hospital laundry was not functioning, and linens were inadequately washed and laid out in the sun to dry. Linens used in septic cases were thrown in with the others, and infection spread throughout the hospital on "clean" linen.

Many of the staff knew this to be poor practice, but they had been worn down by refusals of help, many politically based. Therefore, they rationalized that they would do the best they could, and lay the blame for failure on others. At this time, De Vinatea and Falcon alone realized that HOPE could help remedy much of this, not only by example but also by additional pressure upon the Ministry of Health in Lima, whose official blessings we bore to Trujillo. Many staff members feared only for their private practice, and the threat from our staff of better service. They reasoned that if HOPE had better results, then they themselves would be judged incompetent, and those patients who could afford private care would flee to Lima rather than risk Belén Hospital.

The problem immediately apparent was: How could we bring about a change in Belén unless we were invited to work there? As long as Acuña continued to feel as he did, as long as he was resistant to change, our task was hopeless. We could train technicians on the ship, and thus make it possible for Falcon to get his long-desired blood bank. We might even be successful in overcoming resistance from Lima, and initiate a nurses' training program. However, unless we could break through the resistance of the leaders of the medical profession in Belén Hospital, our long-range mission would fail.

As young Dr. Salazar, a highly trained surgeon, took us through the wards, he pointed out case after case of extensive third-degree burns. Some covered two thirds of the surface; others disfigured the face beyond recognition. While no plastic work had been done for these cases, the very fact that they were alive indicated a good technical knowledge on the part of the medical staff. We were told that the majority of the burns were the result of convulsive seizures of unknown cause, which occurred while the patients were preparing food over open pans of hot cooking oil. Losing consciousness, they would fall into the oil, tipping the pan and its boiling contents over the entire body. This opened a possible area of neurological research that we were to look into later. But at this time there was no trained neurologist working in Trujillo, despite the many cases of convulsive disorders.

In the pediatric wards, it was not unusual to find two and more children to a bed. Hospital officials had no choice; they were working in a hospital constructed with the normal population of a town of forty thousand in mind. However, an additional forty thousand more destitute people were now living in barriadas that ringed the inner city. Their children needed care. These physicians of Trujillo were responding in the only way available. Everywhere in the wards were toddlers with swollen bellies and skinny legs so common to kwashior-kor, or protein-deficiency starvation. Others, rigid in the almost decerebrate state accompanying meningitis, lay in wards along with other children. Isolation was impossible. The chief of pediatrics explained that "at least we keep these cases alone in a bed."

In the obstetrics ward there were frequently two mothers to each bed, and they remained only just long enough to have their babies before immediately returning to an overcrowded house or straw barriada lean-to with a dirt floor.

These, and so many other similar scenes, would seem more than enough to depress us; but, on the contrary, they made us forget the signs ordering us to go home. They made us realize how important it was that we stay. The difficulties under which the physicians of Trujillo operated only made us respect them, not look down on them. We realized that perhaps their distrust might stem from a reluctance to arouse false hopes, only to have them dashed later. They had no way of proving in advance that we were there to help solve their problems, not add to them. But the determined faces of the HOPE staff told me that before the year was over the inscriptions on the wall would change from *Yanqui no* to *Yanqui sí!*

[5]

Later that same afternoon I met with Dr. Jorge de Vinatea and
Craig Leman to discuss the problems not only of organization
but also of meeting possible resistance from the medical
students, pressured by Communist student leaders at the university. The nursing ministry, too, was not cooperating, perhaps because they felt they had been slighted by Cabby when
the program was beginning, or because Nancy Campion had
gone ahead in Lima without their assistance. In any case, they
were not about to assign nurses or students to the ship.

Jorge was particularly concerned over the student problem.
He advised us that the students had warned him that we were
not to undertake the milk program in the barriadas. The fame
of the ship's Iron Cow and its flowing protein had preceded
us: milk from powder and seawater was indeed a modern
miracle. The Communists had indicated they would cooperate
if we permitted them to control milk distribution. We could
not consent to this; it would have been morally wrong to give
in to this kind of pressure. It would also have given the local
Communists a chance to pose as benefactors, or even to
contaminate the milk and then accuse us of working with the
oligarchy to poison the poor.

I refused even to consider the request, and was solidly
backed by Craig Leman. Instead, we determined upon an
alternate course, that of distributing milk through the schools,

including those in the barriadas. This would call the bluff of
the Communists, who would be forced to stage a riot to
prevent the hungry from getting the precious, much-needed
milk. Jorge agreed to pass on our decision, and also suggested
that we meet with the student leaders promptly and discuss
the entire program. There was no way to avoid this, since the
students in Peru have a 50 percent vote at all faculty councils.
It is within their power to close a school with or without a riot,
cause the dismissal or election of a faculty member, decide
upon admission procedures and, above all, influence the curriculum.

This is not always all bad, as we later discovered. The power
of the students developed as a means of forcing modernization
of curriculum and improving teaching methods by ridding the
universities of oligarchs who refuse to accept a changing
world. Unfortunately, any action against the existing order is
considered Communist-inspired, and it is true that the Communists have organized small activist groups that frequently
have a dominant position. When the students clamor for a
constructive change, the Communists take advantage of their
youthful exuberance and precipitate a full-fledged riot out of
what began as an orderly demonstration or appeal. Therefore,
we should not condemn out of hand all student protests
because we have seen in our own country much the same
techniques used to distort a constructive and moral purpose.

In Trujillo we found that the younger faculty members who
were interested in modernizing the medical school were popular with the students, regardless of their politics. The older,
more rigid faculty members who would not listen to the cry for
change were in trouble. We ourselves were in the middle.
Unless the dilemma were solved, the potential losers would be
the Peruvian people.

The nursing situation was more serious. Dorothy Aeschliman
was beside herself. "Dr. Walsh, if we don't get the students,"

she told me, "we simply cannot function. Certainly we won't be able to open all of the *Hope's* wards and we can't send any nurses ashore." Her eyes watered as she talked, and her lips stiffened with emotion. "Don't these people realize we're here to help them? I'll never understand why they act this way. They can't do the job themselves and they won't let us do it!"

"I know, Dottie," I replied. "We'll work it out even if we have to use nurse auxiliaries for training. The military services have promised us nurses, and we have six trainees coming from Bolivia. These six are graduates. We simply have to get started. They'll see the light soon enough. You'll go along, won't you?"

"You know we will," she answered quietly. "Our girls were picked because they could teach. But they'll work around the clock on the wards if they have to. It just makes me so darned mad. We have to teach them to help themselves, or this part of our lives is wasted. Sure, we can get started. But I don't know how long we can last without help. Even after they begin training, it will be weeks or perhaps months before we can leave them free on the wards." Shaking her head, she bit her lips to stop herself from crying as she turned away.

This situation was explained to Jorge de Vinatea at our meeting, and he shook his head in disgust at the attitude in Lima. "Please," he said, "do not be too harsh in your thinking toward the nursing authorities in Lima. They believe what they are doing is best for the country. They don't realize that we haven't time to wait for the kind of standards they wish to impose. This will come later. Meanwhile, we'll find a solution."

Conferences aboard ship that evening lasted until dawn broke "over the Rock." Many decisions were made, all adding up to a determination to move forward.

At first, we would confine most of our professional activities to the ship in an effort to pressure Lima into assigning trainees.

We knew that we were to receive six from Bolivia, approximately twelve from the town of Tarma (at whose hospital members of our Oroya unit had been working), and a few others from the army. It was reasoned that Dr. Acuña would not accept our "girls" on his hospital wards or in the operating rooms as yet, so for the time being we would defer even trying. Our prime onshore hospital activity would be to expand the outpatient clinic facilities at Belén, in this way giving us subtle exposure to the community and to curious medical students who wished to "look us over." We would meet with the student leaders later. Dr. Arnold Smoller was given the job of organizing the clinics because of his previous experience in that same area in Asia the year before.

Our initial push was to the barriadas, the ring of slum communities surrounding Trujillo. This decision was influenced in no small part by the unrelenting insistence of La-Verne Fakkema of San Francisco, a public health nurse. LaVerne, a tall, somber-faced girl with beautiful but sad eyes, had been working in Trujillo with the advance unit for almost two months before the ship's arrival, and had come to the conclusion that pressure was going to be put on us to give preferential treatment to the more fortunate of the community. Although this was contrary to our philosophy, she was convinced that political motives could overcome our own wishes unless we were firm.

Contrary to all orders, and on her own initiative, she had been making home visits in the barriadas, and had made many friends. She had been overwhelmed at the need of the people and their neglect, and no argument could persuade her to delay her public health program. "What is a barriada?" she asked. "It is people living in misery and filth. There is no water, no sanitation, and disease is everywhere. Malnutrition and tuberculosis are walking hand in hand, and yet these people haven't given up. They want to live. Look at the names they have chosen for their communities: *Esperanza,* which means 'hope,' and *Porvenir,* which means 'future' or 'things to come.' We can't deny people with this spirit because of fear or political expediency.

"Have you ever been inside of one of the homes in a barriada?" she asked. "Let me tell you how they live, and perhaps you'll wonder why they want to live. We were in a typical barriada home yesterday. One room was empty except for the water barrel, and unlighted except for the shafts of sunlight through the door. Magazine covers or old cardboard made a border on the earth-brown walls.

"The only other room must have been used as a kitchen. There was no stove, but there were a wooden crate that served as a bed for a small child, three light chairs, and a shelf holding some primitive cooking utensils. This was the total furniture of the house. Except for the small child, who slept in the crate, the others slept on the ground.

"A mother lived here with her three children, and showed us around as graciously as if it were one of the Merriweather Post homes. Besides her household goods, her three children and the clothes they presently had on their backs, all the mother had was what was in the yard behind the hovel: one square of cloth draped over a tired-looking clothesline, one chicken looking for a crumb, and a green vine of some sort encircling a stake.

"We asked Señor Burgos, unofficial mayor of Esperanza and our guide, how they cooked—when they had something to cook. 'Those who can afford it,' he replied, 'use a pan of charcoal or a kerosene flame. Some have kerosene lamps or candles for light at night.' "

Henry Ricci, an ophthalmologist from San Angelo, Texas, asked with a trace of bitterness, "How do they bury the dead?" LaVerne said Burgos had told her that "every one who can contributes a little toward the burial. The body is often put into a wooden carton, but if there is not enough money for such a box it will be put in a pasteboard carton and then taken to the cemetery."

Her arguments were compelling, so we decided to experiment first in a small area, Otiniano, neither symbolically named nor as heavily populated as the others. Only about twelve hundred of the total barriada population of almost forty thousand lived in Otiniano. LaVerne agreed to coordinate our efforts with local public health authorities, and our "assault plans" were ready.

Otiniano's streets were narrow and dirty. There was no electricity, and water had to be brought in from the outside. After dark, all activity in Otiniano ceased. On the first occasion that LaVerne took me to visit there, I heard on every side the racking, dry coughs that told all too clearly that tuberculosis was taking its toll, spreading from shack to shack, a danger to the entire city of Trujillo. Was it any wonder the barriada people were resented? Yet, as LaVerne pointed out, nothing was being done to improve the situation.

LaVerne showed what one determined nurse can do. She found an unused portable X-ray unit in the headquarters of the public health officer. Asked why he wasn't using it to case-find in Otiniano, he simply shrugged and said, "No electricity." Undaunted, LaVerne called upon the city fathers, using the influence of the ubiquitous archbishop, who would soon take on a more significant role in our mission. She convinced them that it was their obligation to put electric lines into the barrio—at no cost to its inhabitants. She committed Project Hope to providing necessary X-ray technicians, films, and any medication necessary to treat those found to have active disease. Within days a survey was under way.

The people of the barrio were so pleased that they cleared out the largest shack available, and while some made benches, others put together rough tables. The day the survey began was one of fiesta and ceremony. We were virtually mobbed by the people, as were the Trujillians who had helped to make all this possible. A turning point had come in their lives—they had discovered that someone really wanted them; someone was concerned with their tomorrow. The children laughed, parents cried, and the elders looked on in disbelief.

There are two endings to this tale. Instead of the 8 percent infected with active tuberculosis anticipated by the health officer, X-ray findings uncovered closer to 35 percent—unfortunately, most of them children. The infected were placed under treatment immediately, and an education program for the entire barriada was promptly instituted.

LaVerne was not content to stop there. Noting that the gratitude of the people had made a deep impression on the officials of Trujillo, she asked that the electric lines remain as a gift to the barriada. Her purpose was a simple one. The X-ray room was to be converted into a classroom so that by day the children could be taught to read, and by night, thanks to the new magic of light, adults could also be instructed. Instead of "Pancho, bring me the pen of your aunt," the reading lesson was "Pancho, boil the water before you drink it."

The city readily agreed to make no charge for installation or service for the first three months. After that, the people of the barrio were to maintain a fund to pay their electric bill for the X-ray reading room.

LaVerne's determination was a lesson in charity, public health, and self-help, democracy at its best.

The university students, too, were impressed, and some volunteered to help and to teach. They looked at us differently now, still reserved but anxious to talk. They found it difficult to believe that the "gringo" was really interested in change. This attitude was to be one of the biggest obstacles to our acceptance in Latin America.

Here we are, a nation able to merchandise almost anything

better than anyone else. Where else can food be sold *because* of its lack of food value? Where else can we sell bread containing added vitamins to step up an *already* vitamin-rich diet? We construct automobiles *not* to last, and in the event they do, we change the style to stimulate replacement by a newer model. Yet in Latin America we have permitted Communists to merchandise, identify themselves with, and *own* the word "change." The have-nots of all nations, and particularly the youth of these nations, use the words "change" and "progress" synonymously. We, and the Western European nations, are identified with the *status quo*, while Communists have usurped the mandate to direct the move forward.

Therefore, the students were amazed that we of HOPE had already fought for and effected change in Trujillo. Archbishop Pérez Silva was delighted. He told me that he felt "we had been sent by the Lord Himself" to help him make the people of the *Norte* realize that change was overdue. The politically astute Señor Cox Larco, a former Governor of Lima who would soon become a patient aboard the *Hope,* came forth to help us. Marcella de Ganoza marshaled the women of Trujillo into a group of volunteers that would never fail us. A peaceful revolution had taken place overnight, and it was the determined dedication of the Fakkemas, the Rodens, the Aeschlimans, and so many others, who had brought it about.

We did not stop at Otiniano. LaVerne had more targets. The next was Porvenir barriada and our entry here was spearheaded by a polio immunization team. Lester Luz, a San Francisco pediatrician, had organized the details with the assistance of the students at the medical school. Fernando Aznoran Vega, a fifty-year student, was a resident of Porvenir and the secretary of the local group for self-improvement in the barriada.

Aznoran and two of his classmates who were studying to become pediatricians had told Luz: "We know that as our children are, so our nation will be. Malnutrition is widespread, infant mortality high, and preventable disease is not being prevented. Many mothers go to a *curandero*, the Peruvian version of the 'medicine man' without medical training. They do not bring the children to trained physicians until it is too late, and the children are either at the point of death or maimed forever. Certainly, it is easier and cheaper to prevent sickness than to cure it."

He found a sympathetic ear in Dr. Luz. Les had only recently returned from Piura, a community farther north. He and some of our advance staff had been called in to help in a polio epidemic that had hit that city almost overnight.

A call to our Washington office brought immediate help in the form of fifteen thousand doses of trivalent Sabin oral vaccine, donated by the Lederle Company. Panagra flew the vaccine in by air express, and many children are walking and living today because of it. But for two weeks, Luz and his team worked under great handicaps day and night, caring for sick children. For example, all unparalyzed limbs had to be tied with gauze restraints against the sides of the beds to keep the children from falling out; there were no guard rails. There were no screens and no way to keep the flies away in the Piura hospital. No isolation technique was practiced, and no physical therapy. The local pediatrician in charge of the hospital explained that they did not have a single full-time graduate nurse. Because of the epidemic, one full-time graduate had been lent to them from another assignment.

Ten days after the vaccinations, the epidemic began to wane. Three children had died within that period; at least nineteen others were to be permanently paralyzed. This is a community of under fifty thousand. When Aznoran asked for the immunization of five hundred children in Porvenir, Les and LaVerne were more than willing.

Bobby O'Grady from Oakland, California; Dorothy Burchett

of Greencastle, Missouri; and Mary Finley from Los Angeles joined them and finished the job within an hour. As Mary tells it:

"The schoolgirls were waiting excitedly in half a dozen rooms lighted only by the sky above. They clapped and smiled as the teams arrived. Later, some of the smaller ones cried as they were ushered toward the frightening looking needles. As always, they were more scared than hurt."

Aznoran and his fellow students knew that five hundred more children would now have a better chance to contribute to the future of their country. Les and his team had the satisfaction of helping these students fulfill a part of their dream.

The final and largest target was Esperanza, the barriada HOPE!

Once again LaVerne was in the vanguard, but now reinforced by many disciples. It would be wrong to say that our Miss Fakkema was popular with the staff. At first she was a "loner," and appeared convinced that she alone saw the problems before us. How wrong she was, and yet how right for Trujillo, for HOPE, for all of us. The success of the barriada program needed someone who looked neither to the right nor to the left, but only straight ahead. Others followed, and indeed at times even salvaged her mistakes, but LaVerne's almost selfish sense of purpose was the motivating force.

Many a time Archie Golden swore that he would not work again with "that woman," but, pediatrician and compassionate human being that he was, he always returned to "her" barriada clinics for more of the same.

The population of Esperanza was estimated to be somewhere between twelve thousand and fifteen thousand people, many of whom had come down from the mountains, lured by promises of an easier life in the city. Food and jobs were waiting, they were told—sometimes by Communist agitators—and there was no need to scratch out a living from a farm on an Andean slope. Loaded into trucks provided by the same agitators, they had descended on Trujillo by the thousands. They found no jobs and no homes, only much resentment from the people of this northern city. Like the squatters from our own Depression days, they threw up a mud and straw settlement of their own on the outskirts of Trujillo. Some found work; they organized, and then elected their own village council and a sort of mayor—Señor Burgos, a schoolteacher. He represented them to the city, and something resembling a truce resulted. They had no water, although it was there, about seventy feet down in the ground beneath them. They brought disease, unemployment, and all the problems that accompany any "squatter" compound. Yet these people had a special quality, a desire to help themselves if only given the opportunity. They set up their own schools, had town meetings, and attempted to cope with their problems. Lack of medical care was one of them, and this is where HOPE found its mission.

LaVerne, Arnie Smoller, and Archie Golden got together with Señor Burgos. A clinic must be set up in Esperanza, but self-help must be the key or the clinic would not work. Esperanza was a good ten miles from the ship, and we had to have a place to work. There were blocks and blocks of streets as wide as a football field, covered with sand as deep as you will find on any beach. One could hardly see the end of the rows of mud and adobe dwellings, each house bursting with occupants. The streets always seemed empty except for an army of dogs of every variety, constantly nosing about the garbage that was everywhere. Rats swarmed, and their size made us wonder if dog ate rat, or vice versa.

All this was a stone's throw from the beautiful city of Trujillo—yet it was another world. This was the site chosen by HOPE to demonstrate self-help and cooperation. The task seemed insurmountable, and would have been but for the people themselves, determined to have a better tomorrow.

[6]

I am tempted to begin the account of our Oroya group, which had been on the scene some two months before the *Hope*'s arrival at Salaverry, with the well-worn cliché ". . . meanwhile back at the ranch . . ." A further temptation is to skip over it quickly, for the Oroya venture was to prove the least fruitful undertaking of the Peruvian mission. This was not the fault of its organizers and supporters, and certainly the dedicated members of HOPE's advance unit cannot be blamed for its failure. In fact, some of the most valuable personal insights gained anywhere resulted from this experience, and despite the ultimate frustration, the Oroya Hopies emerged wiser, though sadder. In the end, it turned out that all problems encountered elsewhere in Peru were in Oroya magnified out of all proportion, and distrust, conflict, and outside pressures finally prevented our continuing with any effectiveness in the mountain town.

The original division of our advance group was based mainly on age because the altitude in La Oroya is some 13,500 feet, and it was felt the younger doctors and nurses could more easily make the adjustment. Chief city of Junín Department, Oroya is also the home of the American-owned and managed Cerra del Paso, one of the largest mineral producers in all South America. The miners are mostly mestizos, who are adequately paid and have the further advantages of the company hospital and company store. Other Indians in the area find a meager existence on mountain farms or as workers on big haciendas.

Many years before, when sulphur fumes from the mine had devastated thousands of acres of the surrounding Sierra and left previously fertile green fields a chalky wasteland, Cerra del Pasco—to make amends—had purchased the ravaged land from the Indians. Soon afterward corrective measures were taken, primarily by raising the height of the stacks in the smelting plant so that the fumes disappeared harmlessly over the horizon. It was unfortunate that this solution had not been previously discovered.

The company still retained all this land and had resisted for years efforts by both the Indians and the Peruvian Government to either seize it or return it to the people. One can drive for miles in Junín Department and see acres and acres of unfarmed grassland, yet there are Indians who are starving. The company finally developed a sheep ranch so that (according to the Peruvians) some excuse could be provided for not releasing the land to the Indians.

None of this had helped the American image; and the hard-core Communists in the area—of which there are many—were gradually convincing the Indians that the original blighting of the land had simply been a Yankee imperialist trick to enable the gringos to steal their fields at a low price.

It was at the troubled heart of this unrest that half our advance group was to find its first home in Peru.

I went along on the train trip, which took us first up the side and finally the spine of the Andes. The little train sometimes gave the impression that it was virtually climbing a vertical line; periodically, it would come to an area where it would have to back up on a side track and get going again with a little downhill start in order to make the next rise. At each stop Indians in bright costumes came to the windows to sell corn, potatoes, and fruit to the passengers. The higher we went, the redder the faces became, not only those of the Indians but of some of our own group as well.

Cabby, the only Peruvian in the lot, had warned us of *soroche,* the famous altitude sickness of the Andes. Newcomers were not supposed to walk rapidly or even carry a suitcase for fear of shortness of breath. Circulatory difficulties such as polycythemia, a rapid increase in the number of red blood cells, could result. However, the only one on the entire trip who asked the conductor for oxygen was Cabieses himself, and by the time we reached the 15,000-foot level he was beet-red and groggy. All the rest of us, including Gloria Aguilera, Priscilla Strong, Will Pirkey from Denver, Colorado; Charlie Isaac from the plains of Kansas, Dave Durham from Wilmington, Delaware; John Stewart and Bryce McMurry from Seattle, Washington; Tom Burns from Pennsylvania, Brooks Hurd and Ed Hamilton from Columbus, Ohio; and John Griffith from Aurora, Colorado, followed instructions to the letter and withstood the trip quite well.

When we arrived in La Oroya, it was a beautiful day, but as we stepped from the train, the sulphur fumes burned our eyes and our nostrils. Disregarding instructions and carrying our suitcases, we soon found that forewarnings were not to be disregarded. After walking only fifty feet at a slightly rapid pace to greet Arturo Vassi, I found that it took me almost thirty minutes to breathe normally again.

Arturo had brought two Apache station wagons, our transportation from the station into the city. Vassi, his husky voice never still, did all that he could to make us feel welcome, but, like so many Peruvians he drove much too fast, and rarely looked where he was going.

As for the town itself, Henry Pendergrass of Boston, one of our later La Oroya participants, aptly described how we all felt: "I have had an opportunity to visit many mining towns in

Many thousands like this little Peruvian girl were the concern of Project HOPE during its year-long stay in her country.

ABOVE: *Hope* at anchor in Salaverry harbor. The mist-shrouded "Rock" looms in the background. BELOW: Dr. Anne Watkins, a specialist in pediatrics from the University of California, examines a patient in the Barriada Esperanza clinic. Behind her is a Mormon volunteer interpreter.

ABOVE: Peruvians wait to be examined at HOPE's Esperanza clinic.
BELOW: Nurse Madaleine Schopfer of Panorama City, California,
holds a young patient reacting to her first vaccination just as
children do everywhere.

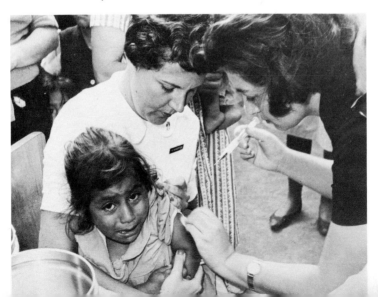

Dr. Harry J. Deeths of Canoga Park, California, and a Peruvian public health nurse inoculate children in the Esperanza clinic.

Dr. Walsh, with (left to right) LaVerne Fakkema of Los Angeles, Madaleine Schopfer, and Dr. Deeths, makes the rounds of Esperanza.

ABOVE: A HOPE nurse interviews a patient in a barriada clinic.
BELOW: Nurse LaVerne Fakkema and Dr. Walter Lentino of Middletown, New York, represent HOPE at Barriada Otiniano's ceremony honoring the project.

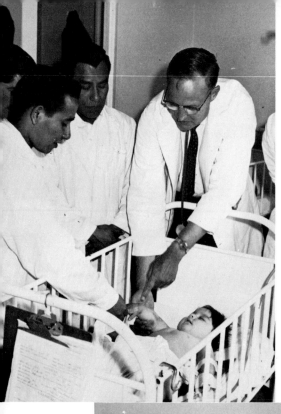

Dr. James S. Vedder of Marshfield, Wisconsin, and Peruvian pediatricians examine a baby at Belén Hospital, Trujillo.

Nurse Mary Jane Damuth of Utica, New York, and Dr. Alexander Gerber of Alhambra, California, make rounds with Peruvian surgeons at Belén Hospital.

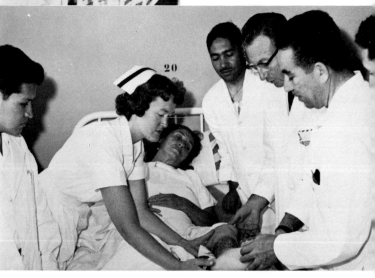

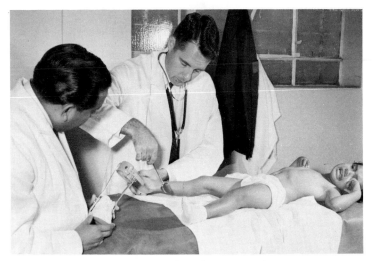

ABOVE: Dr. Donnel D. Etzwiler of Minneapolis, Minnesota, examines a patient at the HOPE clinic in Belén Hospital while his pediatric counterpart observes the American doctor's technique. BELOW: Dr. Walsh, a heart specialist, checks a young patient with the classic heart disease called "blue baby" at Belén Hospital.

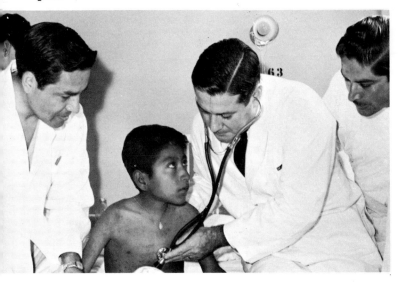

Hopie Vivian Crosswhite of the Mayo Clinic pours milk for young Peruvians, many of whom had never tasted it before.

ABOVE: Nurse Ann Roden (left) of South Bend, Indiana, joins children at a combined orphanage and day-care school in Trujillo, one of many points for milk distribution. Many nurses visited the school to play and dance the Twist with the children. BELOW: Children of Trujillo leave school after receiving their daily carton of milk manufactured aboard S.S. *Hope* by its renowned Iron Cow machine from desalinized water, powdered milk and anhydrous fat.

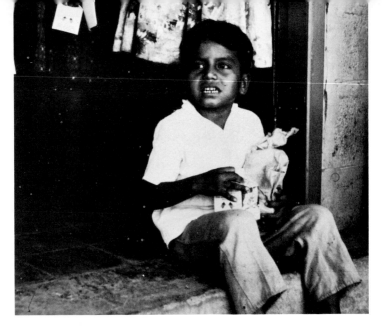

ABOVE: One Peruvian boy waits to share with his family the treasured gift of milk. BELOW: Nurse Mary Munton of Albany, New York, checks a patient with Pott's disease (tuberculosis of the spine). The boy at right has had cleft-lip surgery.

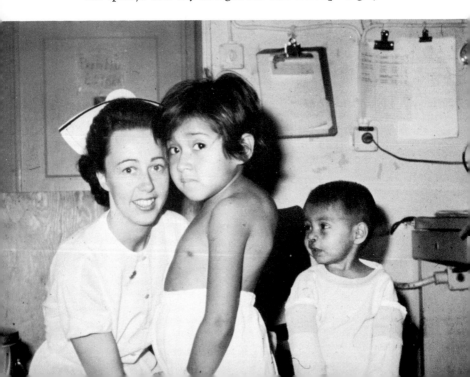

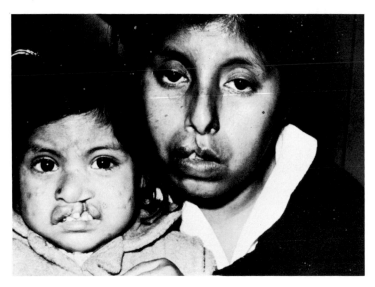

ABOVE: *Before:* A Peruvian mother and her child come aboard the S.S. *Hope* for cleft-lip surgery. BELOW: *After:* Mother and child relax in the *Hope's* pediatrics ward during postoperative care period.

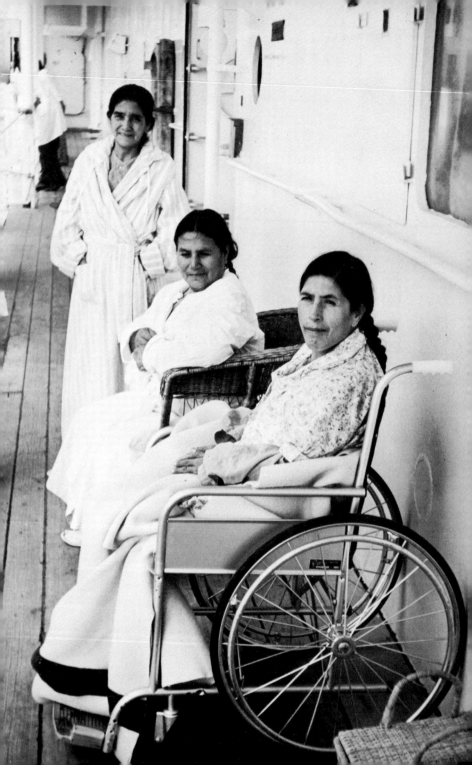

ABOVE: HOPE nurses Mary Finley of West Covina, California (left), Mary Munton (right), and Peruvian volunteer Maria Cristina check the progress of four cleft-lip repair babies in the pediatrics ward. BELOW: Dr. Arno Gurewitsch of New York City instructs a class in physical therapy aboard the floating medical center.

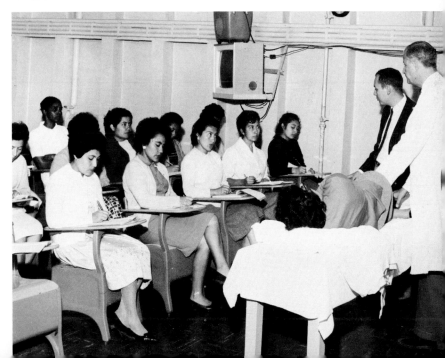

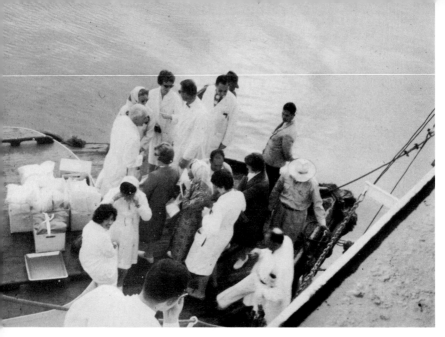

ABOVE: A HOPE medical team leaves the ship to treat and examine patients in shore hospitals. Severe and instructive cases will be sent aboard for more detailed examinations and treatment or surgery. BELOW: Mothers visit their children in S.S. *Hope*'s pediatrics ward.

ABOVE: Pediatrics nurse Ann Roden takes a young patient for a promenade on deck. With them is Dr. Archie S. Golden of Baltimore, Maryland. BELOW: Outpatients leave the hospital ship.

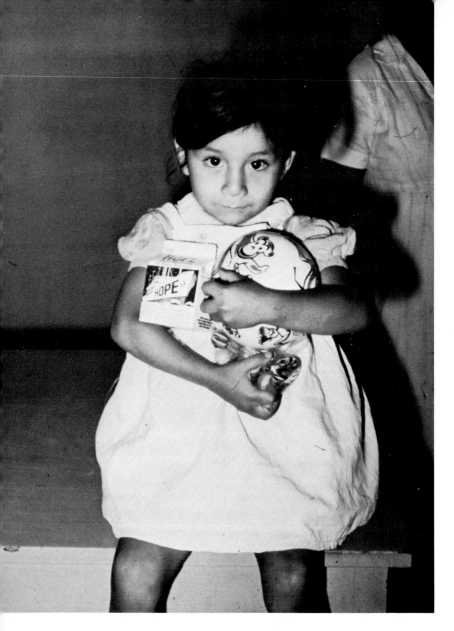

A little girl ready to leave S.S. *Hope* after hospital care. She holds a carton of milk and the traditional toy given all children treated on board.

Pennsylvania and West Virginia, but in none of these was I so
overwhelmed by the squalor and unattractiveness as I was
with La Oroya. In the lower half of La Oroya and in old La
Oroya, which is downwind on the opposite side of the river,
there is a penetrating smell of something like sulphuric acid.
. . . I am told that the wind blows in the opposite direction
only about three days a year. All the white-collar workers and
executives of the mines have homes built upwind away from
this very unpleasant and overwhelming exhaust from the
smelters. As I approached the hospital itself, which was the
same drab color as the surrounding mountains, I thought to
myself that this must surely be a prison or a reformatory. It
was a three-story building of the grimmest architecture. It was
actually divided into two parts, with the larger and more
unattractive portions as living quarters for the physicians and
their families and for the nurses."

The Obrero hospital of La Oroya rested almost at the foot of
a mountain white as chalk from the oppressive fumes that
Pendergrass described. The whole area was cold and damp.

Though our group immediately became depressed, we still
felt that we were needed. We found that Vassi had been
carried away by his own enthusiasm and that the people with
whom we spoke had little knowledge of English or of our
purpose in being there. By a quick vote we nominated Gloria
Aguilera, forever after known as Mamasita, to be our negoti-
ator, press secretary, interpreter, translator, and goodwill ambassador. Gloria was pretty, dark, determined, happy, and
spoke fluent Spanish. She saw in La Oroya more challenge
than depression, and to a greater degree than any of us was
willing to give Vassi the benefit of the doubt.

After showing us to our quarters, which were not too
uncomfortable, it became apparent that Vassi wished us to
stay here much longer than we had planned. Our intention was
to give La Oroya a hand until the ship arrived. Thereafter we

would offer only consultant help. The sparkling new refrigerator, new furniture, and repaired plumbing made it apparent that others had quite different ideas, including a plan to have us work from time to time in four other hospitals in the area.

That evening we found that there was a new hospital in the city of Tarma, which lay many miles away in the Andes but was still part of Junín Department. This monument to politics had been built by General Odria when he was President as a tribute to his home town. It was lavishly equipped (like so many pork-barrel projects in our own country) but staffed only by a few low-salaried physicians from Lima, and unused by the local physicians and patients of the area.

We were taken to see the Tarma hospital the next afternoon following lunch, traveling both by car and a bus chartered for us from the Nido de Águilas (Nest of Eagles) Company. It was a long ride, but the country became greener and, as we approached the rim of Tarma Valley, suddenly breathtaking. Here we passed an Indian wedding; being typically American, we stopped to take pictures for the folks back home. The Indian maidens were dressed beautifully in innumerable skirts and strangely shaped hats, each style indicating family origin. Skirts flashed brilliantly in the sun as the entire wedding party danced off down the road to the lovely high notes of many flutes. The more skirts, the greater affluence. A status symbol, Peruvian style.

The city of Tarma, nestled in one of the most fertile valleys of Peru, is beautiful—and so is its almost patientless hospital. During our visit there, Gloria saw a group of Indians standing silently across the street with a wooden coffin in their hands. They had evidently come to call for a deceased relative. We were to learn later that the local Indians thought one went to the hospital only to die. After seeing a surgeon run out of the operating room during an acute appendectomy and go down the corridor for an extra instrument before returning to resume surgery, I could not help wondering at the wisdom of the Indians.

Some ninety miles below La Oroya, in the opposite direction from Tarma, was the Daniel Carrion Hospital in Huancayo. We were told that they, too, expected our staff to work there, as did still a fourth hospital, Chulec, operated by the Cerro del Pasco Company. This was under the direction of Dr. Kurt Helreigel, capably assisted by Dr. Lunborg, an American physician from Vermont, who had been there for five years. This was the finest hospital in the area, but it was limited to families of the employees of the mining company.

It soon became obvious to us that one of the most useful services we could render would be to improve relationships between the Peruvian physicians of high caliber who were employed at Chulec and the ten rather mediocre men then at the Obrero hospital in Oroya. The difference in pay was depressingly great, as was the intellectual gulf between the two staffs. The physicians in the Obrero were paid approximately $100 a month and were expected to work only four hours a day. At noon they began their siesta; then from three to seven they were permitted to see their private patients. But all those who could afford private facilities in La Oroya were cared for at the company hospital, a situation that further embittered the Obrero physicians against both the Chulec staff and the gringos who employed them. We were never able to persuade the two staffs to work together.

Notes in Gloria Aguilera's diary reflect our experiences in La Oroya. She writes:

Once back in La Oroya we settled into our quarters. We'd been assigned the apartment ordinarily used by the General Medical Superintendent. It was spacious and attractive and we had two employees assigned to look after us. Because I was the only one who could speak to them, I inherited the job of housemother, or "mamasita." This responsibility included such

activities as ordering food and planning menus; trying to teach
the cook to occasionally prepare an American menu or at least
to cut down on the peppers and onions so that our esophagi
would not be cauterized; keeper of the "kitty" for extras such
as chocolate, jams and jellies which were not available from
the hospital kitchen; linen counting; sanitation supervisor and
social secretary. I never realized that growing up in New
Mexico would qualify me as a "mamasita" at the crest of the
Andes.

Mealtimes were fun. We generally ate together, and any
invitations we received usually included all of us. Breakfast
and lunch were generally casual. Pris [Priscilla Strong, our
nurse anesthetist] always tried to be a little more dressed up
for the evening meal, no matter how weary we were. All took
turns saying grace, each in the words of their own religion.
Conversation was always animated as we covered the successes and failures of the day in a sort of group therapy. The
doctors were most grateful for our efforts to provide decent
meals. Although they were all senior to me by many years, I
really began to *feel* like a house mother.

Our efforts to help matters at the Obrero hospital in some
ways probably made them worse. For example, we explained
that we had not come six thousand miles to work a four-hour
day: our physicians wanted to work full days both in the
clinics and in conferences. Our nurses, too, wanted to do what
they could in an eight-hour day of teaching and improving the
nursing curriculum. We soon found that the only physicians
attending our conferences were those from Chulec, whose
good sense and schedule enabled them to take the time to
improve their medical knowledge. We were the only ones at
work at our afternoon clinics and we found we had become a
service organization rather than a teaching unit. We realized
that the Obrero physicians had to work at the afternoon clinics
without pay, but we felt that since we had come as volunteers
thousands of miles to help them, they owed us their attention.
We tried everything we could to encourage the Obrero doctors
to change their habits, but to no avail.

One of our nurses was on duty at a clinic when a patient with an obvious acute appendicitis presented herself. Our nurse summoned the "on call" local physician, but since it was siesta time he refused to come. Finally, at about six o'clock, the patient, who was in severe pain and becoming rapidly worse, was honored by his visit. He was dressed for a fiesta. Siesta-to-fiesta seemed to be the everyday habit in La Oroya. He looked at the girl, agreed on the diagnosis, said that he was going to a party, and would take care of her in the morning. Despite the entreaties of others present, nothing was done, and at two o'clock that morning the appendix perforated, the patient developed peritonitis, and was dead by the time the fun-loving surgeon returned.

It was not unusual to see patients with compound fractures of the leg lie unattended in the hospital for ten days to two weeks. Not only were they unattended; they were given nothing for their pain. Other patients remained in the hospital as much as a month without a note being written on their charts or a medication given them. Yet there were five surgeons on the staff of the hospital, and only enough work for two of them.

Vassi kept his word to the extent that whatever equipment we recommended, he did purchase, but he took to spending less and less time in La Oroya. This was more than a little demoralizing, but we persevered in the hope that Gloria might make headway with her nursing program and that Brooks Hurd, our pathologist, could bring the pathology lab to some semblance of functioning order.

Nursing projects fared best. The chief nurse at Obrero, Teresa Vera, developed an excellent relationship with Gloria. Thus an in-service education course for nurses' aides was initiated. Gloria planned the course, but it was the staff nurses at La Oroya who did the actual teaching. It was so successful that it lasted for six months after we had left the hospital, and provided a cadre to help the overburdened Peruvian nurses.

Student nurses at Tarma Hospital were prepared for their later affiliation aboard the ship. Classes were held to orient them to the methods and techniques utilized on the *Hope*, and they proved later to be the outstanding group of trainees.

We tried to introduce more modern techniques in the operating rooms, such as the use of sterile packs and instrument setups, along with more careful handwashing by scrub nurses and physicians.

The greatest disappointment to the nurses was the failure of the Obrero hospital to set up a demonstration unit in the obstetrics wing. They felt that here they could initiate procedures that could then be followed throughout the hospital, indoctrinate personnel on new procedures, and demonstrate proper sterile technique. They worked for days preparing their plans, and even had them approved by the ever-enthusiastic Dr. Vassi, but there was no follow-through, and after four months of entreaty the girls reluctantly abandoned the project.

Not all of our experiences in the mountains were grim. We had our comic relief as well. I shall never forget, for example, when Cabby and Vassi told me that I had to make a tour of the various communities, to be received by the mayor and given a certificate or decoration for bringing medical care to the area.

Of course, part of this program was Vassi's desire to pressure us into a permanent commitment to La Oroya. The other motivation was purely political, emanating from Lima, to demonstrate to the people of the area that the Ministry of Health was trying to do something to improve their lot.

Because my Spanish was miserable, as we set out on tour Cabby prepared a very simple speech for me, starting with, "Excusen mi mal Español" (translated, "Excuse me for my bad Spanish"). We scattered the words for "work together" throughout the next few lines, and then I would sit down to the loud applause of the Town Council and favored guests who were invited. This speech was customarily given in response to the mayor's spirited address, which usually followed the singing of the Peruvian national anthem by the town's outstanding soprano, accompanied by a creaky phonograph. Since I understand Spanish no better than I speak it, either Vassi or Cabby was supposed to sit beside me, and nudge me when I was supposed to reply.

In the town hall of Huancayo our welcome was particularly enthusiastic. The town hall was not only bulging, but loudspeakers were connected so that the entire square, brimming with people, could hear the ceremonies. Gloria Aguilera had taken the trip with us, acting as interpreter, and she was sitting in the first row of the audience.

The soprano on this occasion was particularly shrill. The hall was like an oven, and the mayor's speech seemed endless, although from the "oh"s and "ah"s coming from the audience I gathered it was most impressive. Then he stopped. Vassi, who had been sitting quietly on my left, nudged my elbow, and I arose and went to the podium and made my reply.

Cabieses had edited my speech that day to include local references, and I had memorized it. The audience sitting before me began laughing politely, and finally louder and louder. Gloria was doubled over in her chair. Ham that I am, I thought that I was a real smash, and when I turned to sit down, the entire audience rose. The applause was deafening.

At that moment the mayor quietly returned to the podium and completed the speech he had not yet finished when I began. Unfortunately, Vassi had fallen asleep during the first half, and when the mayor stopped to get a glass of water my friend had given me the signal to go forward. The mayor, being a very polite man, let me finish my remarks before he resumed, not only in the middle of his speech but also, as I later found out, in the middle of a sentence.

From that point on, I discarded my memorized speech and

used Mamasita as a translator for my remarks, presented first
in good old North American.

The people themselves were anxious that we stay, and did
much to make us feel wanted. The unions arranged a festival
with dancing and singing till all hours of the night. We were
invited to the interhacienda sheepgrowers' festival to join in
the traditional *Pachamanca* supper, a sort of Andean version of
the New England clambake, hot stones and all. Funerals and
weddings became a part of our lives, and it was at one of the
weddings that Mamasita met Conrad Nichtawitz, a Swiss
engineer with Cerra del Pasco, whom she later returned to
Peru to marry—one of the four or five weddings between
Hopies and local residents.

In general, however, our experience in La Oroya was not a
good one. With the idea that fresh viewpoints would help, we
began adding and changing personnel. We sent to Oroya three
devoted and willing nurses—Lynn Morrison of Larchmont,
New York; Jennie Bianchi of Elmhurst, New York; and Shirley
Johnson of Oakland, California. Jackie Harris, one of our lab
technicians from Columbus, Ohio, and niece of the U.N.'s
Ralph Bunche, who had a wonderful sense of humor and the
ability to cope with virtually any situation, also went along.
Two physicians accompanied the group. It was interesting to
find that the girls had far greater patience than did our physicians—perhaps because they knew they were to be in Peru for
a longer time or because, at their level, they were able to get
much closer to the people. Later, Jackie related her La Oroya
experience this way:

Obrero hospital, which was to be our area of operations, was
a cluster of slate-colored buildings. The thick stone walls kept
out the warm afternoon sun, and chill pervaded the entire
hospital. The patients wore wool caps; part of the nurses'
uniform was a blue sleeveless sweater. . . .
It was in Oroya that I made a name for myself as the girl

who fell through a glass door. On the morning following our arrival I began to feel the effects of the altitude. I had *soroche*. The symptom which caused the most discomfort was a permanent pain in the right temple. I was perpetually nauseated and breathless. Whenever I dropped off to sleep, I had nightmares. For two days, I languished around like Elizabeth Barrett Browning, convinced that I was malingering. And that everybody else thought so too. Finally, during my third night at 13,500 feet, I got up, fainted in the doorway of the bedroom, and as I fell, broke the glass in the bedroom door. I came to to find a semicircle of HOPE doctors and nurses holding a conference over my flannel-pajamaed self. The result of that conference: nasal oxygen for the patient throughout the night. The next day the headache was gone and with it the nausea, and I felt much better. The only leftover—a month-long head and chest cold. . . .

Soroche was not my only tangle with the altitude. Water boiled here at 85 degrees centigrade, and this was not hot enough to melt most bacteriological media. This also meant that you couldn't make up larger lots of media because they couldn't be remelted in a boiling water bath. I could make up only what I had Petri dishes for. In practical terms this means I had to be constantly concerned with the time-consuming procedure of media preparation and sterilization. The heat of the autoclave not only sterilized the media but completed the dissolving process.

The laboratory had no cans in which to store sterile Petri dishes, so we used a giant soup pot which the kitchen let us have. The autoclave was so plugged with mineral deposits abundant in the mountain water that circulation of steam within the jacket was not always adequate and the pressure gauges were not reliable. We could only hope that the bacteria had also been affected by the altitude and did not mind if their food was overcooked.

And I remember the people who worked so hard at Obrero hospital, people from Lima and other parts of Peru and people from Minnesota, Colorado, California, and Ohio.

My counterpart, Dr. Amelia Olivares, a young physician fresh out of school, was in charge of the laboratory. A shy smiling person, she eagerly bustled around locating supplies we would need for a bacteriology laboratory. Taking time from her pediatrician husband and two little girls, she worked late many evenings and holidays as we prepared media and sterile glassware and subjected it to the tender mercy of that obstreperous autoclave.

Shirley Johnson, an O.R. nurse from Minnesota, was my roommate in Oroya. She rose early each morning in order to study Spanish before she went to work. Out of her own pocket, she bought nail files and brushes for the O.R. scrub sinks at Obrero. At night she recruited all of us to help make drapes for the O.R.

Dr. John Griffith, a general practitioner from Colorado, whose thinning crop of hair earned from us the nickname of St. Francis For The Birds, was our chief. In this capacity he backed us in our projects. He gingerly donned the damp surgical gowns (their autoclave was quite a monster too) and backed Shirley in the O.R. He talked to the Peruvian physicians about the institution of a bacteriology laboratory. He gave classes for the nurses. He talked to the local HOPE Committee about the importance of initiating a blood bank at Obrero. In the evenings as we sat around the dinner table, he'd tell us about Jackson Hole, Wyoming. God's country, he'd declare. Nowhere on earth could you get such fried eggs and pancakes, and the fishing was always great. There is so much more I remember: Wrapped in blankets we'd sit around in the living room listening to our one record, "Besame Mucho," as it dutifully rotated on the creaky phonograph—the festive breakfasts with Peruvian nurses on their way from Tarma to the ship—the triumph of sending out our first bacteriology report —the despair when our first batch of TB media containing thirty precious eggs was ruined in the autoclave which we had attempted to use as an insuspator—the mining company store where you could buy strawberry jam and pickles—the straw-filled pillows in which I could never make a hollow for my head—riding back from Tarma on one of those misty mountain evenings when the stars seemed to be just over the next rise in the road.

When I think of Oroya, it is with pain, for I regretted leaving what I felt was an unfinished task. At the same time I realized that my small project had to be subjugated to the overall aims of Project HOPE.

For every frustration met by our physicians, our nurses and technicians had a compensation. This is not to say that their hearts didn't bleed a little every day or that their patience was not tried, but with the influence of Mamasita and, I assume, their own private "bull sessions," they adopted a more comfortable philosophy, acknowledging that change never came overnight.

While the director of nurses at the Obrero hospital became more conscientious and cooperative, Vassi paid less and less attention to our problems.

Dr. Hurd, together with Jackie Harris, had taken a lab that was nothing and made it into something reasonably functional. Ed Hamilton, surgeon from Columbus, Ohio, performed gastrectomies that had been delayed for years, and continued his surgical rounds whether Obrero doctors accompanied him or not.

But as our nurses concentrated more and more in the Obrero unit, our doctors gradually were drifting more frequently from Obrero to Chulec. Morale continued to worsen. An unfortunate action on the part of one of our physicians did little to help matters. There was much deafness in Oroya, and therefore much interest in having one of our men perform necessary surgery to cure selected patients. We were all overjoyed, because this would be such a dramatic and obvious contribution by advanced medical techniques. Our physician returned to the ship, which had just arrived in Lima, to pick up the necessary equipment. The patients waited in vain for him to come back. He made no explanation for his abrupt departure for home from Peru, since he realized that his childishness in striking back at the physicians in Oroya through the patients was inexcusable. It was weeks after the incident that I first learned of it. I was shocked and ashamed. I vowed that that man would never be part of HOPE again.

After the initial experience of our staff in Junín, there was considerable discussion as to whether the program there should be continued. Vassi had succeeded so well in spreading the word of HOPE's efforts (with no small credit to himself) that it would be embarrassing for us to leave without giving it another honest try. In June, once again it was decided to supplement the rotation with some men from the ship after it had arrived.

No HOPE staffer likes to feel that we have ever had a failure. Therefore, Marty Kohn, who had become chief of staff on the ship together with myself and a few other members of the Executive Committee, decided to give La Oroya one more chance. Dick Hahn, a thoracic surgeon, performed several thoracic operations in Tarma. Lobectomies, which become necessary in cases of advanced tuberculosis or cysts, were done in the hospital there. The Peruvians themselves cooperated by changing the chief of the Tarma Hospital. They replaced him with a Dr. Amaya, who was a vast improvement and who seemed to be making a serious effort.

In the Obrero hospital in La Oroya, however, things looked as bad as ever. In X ray a three-foot hole in the wall that let in the dust and dampness was never repaired. In the hospital itself only a third of the beds continued to be occupied despite the great needs of the local people. Vassi announced that since all the recommended equipment had been ordered, his job was finished and he would no longer return to Junín Department. This created serious problems. Our staff felt that Vassi was dumping his job upon them, particularly as the atmosphere and weather worsened. With the election closing in, strikes and violence among the mine workers became a daily routine.

At the same time the group in Trujillo was shorthanded, and felt that if the Peruvian participation was to be brought to the highest possible pitch we should not dilute our effort. We talked the problem over with the whole group.

Although the physicians were thoroughly depressed, the nurses had suddenly become encouraged. Gloria Aguilera almost became ill at the thought of leaving. Lynn Morrison felt that we were admitting defeat and giving in to political pressure. But the decision was ultimately made to return all personnel to the ship so that the bigger job at hand, the fulfillment of our mission in Trujillo, could be successfully carried out.

With our conclusion reached, it fell to Marty Kohn to visit La Oroya just when one of our own nurses, Shirley Johnson, developed acute appendicitis. Marty, whose mission was to advise the Obrero hospital that they had not shown sufficient cooperation to justify our staying, transformed his words into action when he, together with Gloria, insisted that Shirley be operated upon at the Chulec Hospital instead of at the Obrero unit. This caused a furor, and allowed Vassi and some of his colleagues to say that they were insulted by the action.

Actually, as Dr. Kohn has said since, "What else could I do? Would you have let anyone be operated upon in that operating room?" The answer, of course, was No.

The pity of the experience of Junín Department was that so much could have been done had we only had some evidence of cooperation on the part of the local physicians, always excepting Dr. Amaya at Tarma.

I don't believe we were really missed in La Oroya once the shock of our departure passed. Vassi rarely if ever returned to that dismal city. The local physicians continued on their four-hour day, and the smelters at the refinery did not stop giving off their sulphuric fumes.

We do not feel that our entire experience was a loss. The mestizos had seen Americans for what we like to think we really are—thoughtful, purposeful individuals, making an effort to help. Perhaps some of the mining company representatives now realize that their obligation reaches beyond their employees. Perhaps even the surgeon who left his patient to die so that he would not miss the fiesta will wake up at night and think of the condemnation delivered by our clinic nurse.

To each of us who were in La Oroya the problems of Peru,

of Latin America and all its people struck home more closely. The conflicts, the distrusts, the agitation from without were no longer something we imagined. They were something we had lived. We found that the isolated task at La Oroya could not be carried out simply as an appendage of a larger project. If Junín Department is to be helped, the help must come first from the government in Lima and from the Peruvian people themselves. Then and only then can projects like our own really bring lasting improvement. I believe Jackie Harris best summed up our La Oroya experience with the words: "Toward the end of July the Project made the decision to close down operations in the mountains. We had three days' notice to make our preparations, tie up loose strings, say our good-byes, and leave. We left behind so much unfinished work, but also many new friends who promised to continue that work."

The contrast at Trujillo was so great that we sometimes wondered if we were still in the same country.

[7]

Our success with the shore clinics in the barriadas of Trujillo left us free to concentrate our attention on the ship. As soon as we had announced we were ready to receive patients, we were overrun; it was immediately obvious that selection of the most urgent cases would be a major problem.

It was noted that some people of means were appearing at the clinics; and although they had been sent to us by their own doctors, there was the expected flurry of opposition from certain Peruvian physicians, fearful that they might lose private patients. Meanwhile, the Communists attempted to drive a wedge between us and the local doctors. They circulated two rumors: first, that we were really in Trujillo to humiliate the wealthy for not caring for their own poor, and, conversely, that we might even be Communists ourselves, since we would not take the wealthy of the community as patients. Fortunately, we were able to turn these charges to our advantage. After checking with the local HOPE committee, I issued a statement telling the entire community that we were not there to humiliate anyone and that we were certainly not there to discriminate against the wealthy. If they wished to be seen by us, they simply had to follow the same rules as everyone else: come to the clinics, wait their turn, and get clearance from their own physician for consultation. We also advised the press that there would be no segregation of the patients in our hospital wards.

Therefore, when Señor Carlos Cox, former Governor of Lima and a large hacienda owner, came to us as a patient he lay in a forty-bed ward together with workers from his own hacienda in the other beds. The young Señora Guildermeister, whose husband was heir to one of the world's greatest fortunes and owner of Casa Grande, largest hacienda in all Peru, waited her turn in a clinic line for three days along with Indians and mestizos.

Not pleased with this lesson in democracy, the Communists tried another gambit. Another press conference was requested to raise a single question: "Doctor, is it true that you have really been financed secretly by the Protestants of the United States so that you could infiltrate this community and undermine Catholic influence in Peru?" Although I was completely surprised by this tactic, I simply reached into my pocket and pulled out my own rosary beads. Holding them up, I asked, "Does this answer your question?" The conference broke up in a roar of excitement, and forever after the press corps of Trujillo were our fast friends.

The first patient to reach our ship was a close friend and the victim of a tragic accident. During the second night of the ship's stay in Trujillo, Dr. Jorge de Vinatea was brought out by ambulance, his face smashed into an almost unrecognizable mass. He had left the evening conference on board the *Hope* shortly before, and while driving his small European car down the poorly lighted roads toward the city he was overcome with weariness, and drove into the rear of a truck parked on the road. Bleeding profusely, he was trapped in the wreck for more than half an hour before a policeman brought him to the ship.

Preliminary examination showed that several facial bones, including both jaws, were broken. Irwin Small, oral surgeon from Detroit, was in surgery before daylight, and the operating crew, headed by surgical nurse Eileen Murphy of Chicopee Falls, Massachusetts, was ready to go in less than half an hour. Other staff members donated the needed blood, since our own blood bank had not yet been opened, and Jorge, like Humpty Dumpty, was soon being put together again. What a beginning: to have the chairman of the HOPE Committee in Peru admitted as our first patient. Dr. Small did a wonderful job. Jorge always maintained he left the *Hope* far more handsome than when he boarded.

During his twelve-day hospitalization, Jorge observed first-hand the dedication and devotion of our staff, reinforcing his feelings that he had been right in bringing the *Hope* to Trujillo. Nor was his stay without humor. He spent the first three days in the Intensive Care Unit under the watchful eye of Bonnie Goodwin, a nurse from Minneapolis. Bonnie, never short on T.L.C. (Tender Loving Care), had been dutifully injecting Jorge in the same side of the derriere, both for relief of pain and to give him needed antibiotics. She had been told not to turn the patient in order to keep his wired-together face in one position. Bonnie felt she just couldn't make another "hit" into the same side, but some beds on a hospital ship are so situated that reaching over them is nearly impossible. Therefore she asked the patient to hold the syringe while she crawled under the bed, intending to have him pass it over to her on the other side. Unfortunately, her uniform hooked in one of the steel rungs of the springs, and while Bonnie struggled to get loose poor De Vinatea patiently held the syringe. Finally, she lost her cap, and went into a fit of giggling that continued while she tore her uniform half off and backtracked. She had to give up and hit the same side, but by then her quality of mercy was more than strained.

Curiously enough, the next two admissions were from our own staff. Charlie Isaac, the urologist from Newton, Kansas, was sent down from La Oroya with a case of infectious hepatitis, and Priscilla Strong's symptoms of the same disease were diagnosed at the time of Isaac's arrival. Because an epidemic of hepatitis would end everything, a hurry call was sent by radio for gamma globulin in sufficient quantity for the entire staff. The Red Cross responded immediately, and our first mass immunization took place upon one another.

Among our first planned admissions was little black-haired nine-year-old Eugenio. He muttered incoherently through lips and mouth horribly deformed from birth, and wept bitterly, reaching up with a dirty sleeve every so often to wipe away the never ending flood of tears. Mary Damuth, our pediatric nurse from Utica, New York, held him on her lap and dabbed at his tears, making every effort to console him.

"Just think how handsome you're going to be," she told him between pats on the shoulder and the rocking we all know so well. That made him cry harder, since not only was he alone among all the kind gringos but now he was also reminded of his impending surgery.

Nurse after nurse came by to comfort him, but to no avail. Finally, they took him on a walk around the deck, and like all little boys on a big ship for the first time, his curiosity overcame his fear. Now somewhat calmer and more trusting, he was turned over to one of the Peruvian nurses in training on the ship. She simultaneously gave him a swat in the derriere and a hug around the neck, let loose with a torrent of Spanish, and headed him toward the pediatric ward.

A short while later he was found propped up in a bed, showered and in a pair of new pajamas, happily trying to figure out a jigsaw puzzle.

Libby Soule, from Charlotte, North Carolina, told us that the men from the male ward had come over to comfort him. When he saw them in their blue HOPE pajamas, he felt he was not alone.

Eugenio was only the first of many such cases admitted by our oral surgical department. Children the world over are the same, and Eugenio had been teased and taunted because he looked so strange. The thought that he might eventually look and speak like a normal child had not yet occurred to him, although the kindness and affection of both staff and other patients had already made him very happy.

A few weeks later, when Eugenio looked at himself in the mirror, a wide grin replaced his horrible split lips. The tears came again, but this time they were tears of happiness.

May ran into June, and a new problem forced itself on our attention. The anchovies that swarmed around our ship in the thousands were being drawn into our pipes, and rumors swept the ship that they were floating out through the water taps and coming up in the toilets. They were being sucked into the water intake needed for the air conditioning. The captain assured all that if the lights should start to dim, we would clear the harbor and leave it to the anchovies. Meanwhile, every known fish repellent in North America was flown to the ship to discourage them, and gradually we were able to control this unexpected threat.

The people of the city of Trujillo were responding rapidly to the catalytic action of the *Hope*. The president of the Rotary Club, together with Archbishop Pérez Silva, gathered together the leading citizens of the town at a meeting where the archbishop urged them to raise money to support the Peruvian workers and trainees, and to help in the barriada program. Tenny Roselle gathered interpreters from everywhere; Marcella de Ganoza rounded up the counterpart of our own "pink ladies" to work in the wards and assist in the outpatient clinics. Even the imminent election was pushed to the background as an entire community awakened to its responsibility. Señor Victor Julio Roselle, the mayor, provided vehicles for transportation in the barriadas. Señor Ramsey persuaded his Rotary Club members to purchase a Volkswagen bus for the transportation of the medical staff.

The wards were filling rapidly, and we already had a waiting list whose end would never be reached. A pair of twin children, almost a year old, came into pediatrics weighing only about seven pounds each. Lester Luz, Archie Golden, and Anne Watkins, all pediatricians, worked over them day and night to keep them alive. Months later, when they had been returned home fat and happy, we lived through the frustration of seeing one of them brought back with malnutrition complicated by a severe pneumonia. This time neither our skills nor our miracle drugs could save him.

Still other children with congenital heart disease—children who would never have lived to see their teens—filled our clinics and hospital, diagnosed for the first time. They were given more than just hope; they were given life itself.

From the first day, patients came in an unending stream. One youngster really touched all of us. A boy of twelve, he was the last surviving son from a family of six brothers, all of whom had died of the dread and mysterious disease of hemophilia, an inability of the blood to clot. Even a minor injury endangers the life of one who suffers from this disease. He was brought to the ship with a severe osteomyelitis of the thumb on the right hand, draining and bleeding, given up for lost by the local physicians. Mayfield Harris, orthopedic surgeon from Los Altos, California, put out a blood call to the entire ship's staff, then scheduled the youngster for an amputation of the thumb. There was no other choice but to hope that the clotting mechanism of the entire staff would help Dr. Harris to save a life. The surgery went well, and the boy seemed to be making good progress. Healing was slow, but each day he lived was a point for our side. Blood replacement kept ahead of blood loss. Then, suddenly, three weeks after the operation the patient called the ward nurse. He was in severe pain, and his hand had swollen to the size of a small football, hemorrhaging beneath the skin. Eldon Ellis of San Francisco and Herb Bloom of

Detroit took him to the operating room to open the tissues and remove the mass of clots, then do their best to stop the constant oozing. As Herb said, "We dreaded every step on the way to the operating room. When this youngster looked up and said, 'The sun is finally setting,' I had to look away to hide the tears." They worked with the patient all night, while Herb's son Mike, working as a summer volunteer aboard the *Hope*, stayed by the "ham" radio, begging anyone who could hear him for antihemophiliac globulin. He was successful, and our patient's sun did not set that night; he is still alive, three years after that desperate evening.

Meanwhile, Lester Mount, neurosurgeon from New York City, was making another invaluable contribution in another ward on the ship. Our good friend Señor Cox, always referred to as the former Governor of Lima, an office of which he had been very proud, had developed a serious problem. Señor Cox was a cheerful man who entertained beautifully. A few months before the *Hope* arrived, he had noticed some weakness in his right hand. The hand was numb, and occasionally even a glass would slip from it. The local physicians at first felt he might be having a variety of common stroke. Then they began to fear the worst—the possibility of a spinal-cord tumor. Since he was a man of importance, no one dared tell him or suggest an operation. It was urged that he go to the United States to be examined, in that way shifting the responsibility. This suggestion is a favorite solution of Latin American doctors, for while there are physicians of great skill in almost every country, when faced with a patient such as this one it is invariably recommended that he "go to the States." Cox, knowing that the *Hope* was coming to Trujillo, decided to wait. By the time Dr. Mount saw him, his right arm and hand were almost useless. For the first time, proper X rays of the cervical vertebrae were ordered and taken. There was a tumor all right, but as the neurosurgeon explained it to the Peruvian physicians, it was simply a large arthritic mass compressing the nerves leading to the affected extremity. Señor Cox was scheduled for surgery, and Mount chiseled away the mass. After a few weeks of appropriate physiotherapy administered by Vivian Crosswhite, the hand and arm were as good as new.

This made a very dramatic impression upon the community, probably more because of the importance of the patient than because of the successful result. Señor Cox became lavish in his praise of HOPE, and the neurology clinic suddenly became one of our busiest. A young Peruvian surgeon, Dr. Polo, spent the entire year working with our neurologist, Dr. Walter Johnson of San Diego, who, together with his nurse-anesthetist wife, had agreed to give us a year of their professional lives. Following our departure, Dr. Polo spent a year more at the University of Michigan. To this day, the only complete neurological clinic in all northern Peru is at the University of Trujillo. Señor Cox's operation had advanced medicine by many years in this northern department.

The staff also collected fringe benefits as a result of this surgical success. Cox's father, Jorge Cox Valle Riestra, president of the board of directors of the Bank for Agricultural Development of Peru, was so pleased with his son's return to health that he invited many members of the medical staff to Hacienda Chiclín, his sugar-cane plantation near Trujillo. One of the girls, obviously impressed, described the day beautifully:

We proceeded through the desert, past fearfully eroded hills with stone-toothed ridges, and over a bridge of what is the Chicama River three months of the year, but in June an arid depression.

After passing miles of sand and rock, we suddenly saw a long line where irrigation and green trees and crops began. We passed through the Village of Chicamita, and turned left into an avenue shaded by large fig trees. It was cool and moist there.

We came to a white church and a community built around a village green with large statues at each end. In a museum across the green were examples of the culture of the Chimu Mochica Indians of Peru. We saw centuries-old mummies wrapped in cloth that was still in a fine state of preservation; other textiles with colors and patterns remarkably bright, and pottery in the shapes of birds, mammals, and reptiles known to the long-dead Indians.

Horses were brought for all guests who wished to ride. Afterward, there was *almuerzo*, with course after course of strange, delicious Peruvian dishes, including *ceviche de corvina* (which is raw fish with lemon, onions and *aji* peppers), *anticuchos*, the inevitable barbecued cubes of beef heart in hot sauce and served on spits. There was a course of hot tamales served with sweetbread; one of turkey and some strange vegetables that looked like parsnips and sweet potatoes—but were not (probably yucca). The dessert course of delicate pastries was followed by coffee and fresh fruits. Throughout lunch, wines of various kinds were served.

We could well understand why people of this country need three hours for lunch. It seemed to us like a Thanksgiving dinner. In a way, I suppose it was, since it expressed the thanks of Señor Cox for the restored health of his son.

On the teaching side we were making satisfactory progress, but in some areas it was still tough going. The students were coming around, but slowly, and we were awaiting the outcome of the election of the new student leaders. After the Otiniano success, they had pledged their support, but the delay was annoying. Betty Berry, our Director of Nursing Education, had just returned from more conferences in Lima, and was encouraged. As Craig Leman put it: "Our thorniest problem at the moment is that we still do not have anything like an adequate number of Peruvian nurses to work with the ship. The few who have applied wish to work short-term. I am convinced that if we don't get more Peruvian nurses, we will have to function with a greatly reduced number of beds, and eliminate almost all of our shore activity. By working a minimum of a forty-eight-hour week and sometimes sixty, our present staff, plus what Peruvian and Bolivian nurses we have, can barely maintain coverage on floor wards and support little shore activity. I have so advised the Minister of Health."

In short, everything was not coming up roses, yet we had already made a tremendous beginning. We were starting to learn something about ourselves as well. Much depends upon how you talk to Peruvians, and we were now aware that we were too impatient for them to take our suggestions. Yet we could never forget that our ship's mission would last only a year and that unless our Peruvian partners took advantage of the knowledge we offered, we could never fulfill our purpose. While those who had waited so long for help could not understand our anxiety, we who had come so far to give it were unable to comprehend their reluctance to take advantage of every minute.

[8]

Our second team of rotators was really the first to join the ship in Trujillo; the first team had worked in La Oroya and on the mainland in Trujillo. Craig Leman stayed for several weeks so that he could transfer his contacts and experience, along with his responsibility, to Dr. Martin Kohn, internist from San Francisco. Marty, like Craig, had been with us in Indonesia and Vietnam the year before, and he had my every confidence. This year he was accompanied by his wife, Jean, a highly competent pediatrician who played a significant role in the development of our "Esperanza" program. Henry Bodner, a superb urologist from Los Angeles; Tim Lally, a radiologist; and Howard Wescott, an internist and allergist from Englewood, New Jersey, were other veteran members who gave added strength to this group. They had been through the mill the first time around.

By this time Dorothy Aeschliman and Betty Berry had decided to institute a training course for nurse auxiliaries. Though not fully trained nurses, auxiliaries can, if given concentrated instruction and supervision, fill a great void on hospital wards. We knew that the need was so great in Trujillo that many would be employed both at Belén Hospital and at the new Hospital for Teaching and Training still being built.

Trainees in the other categories were plentiful. There were some seventeen laboratory-technician trainees already working; X-ray technicians were in training; and Anita Soto, our blood-bank technician, was at work ashore with Dr. Percy Falcon. Her Spanish was fluent and her understanding of the people themselves even better. Frequently voicing her concern over the restlessness caused by the forthcoming election, she more than anyone was aware of the problems soon to arise.

But even Anita was shocked one day by a lone Communist holding up a sign reading THE GRINGOS HAVE TAKEN EVERYTHING ELSE YOU HAVE. NOW THEY WANT YOUR BLOOD! Thanks to her language fluency, she was able to reassure the Peruvians nearby. At the same time she let loose a torrent of Spanish at her tormentor that would hardly bear repeating. Whatever it was, he fled as she took a step in his direction.

On another occasion Anita was showing a group of Peruvians through the ship when one of the visitors identified himself as a Communist. Learning that Anita was Cuban, he asked her if she was a Fidelista. Not wishing to set off a political discussion, she made no answer. He persisted, and repeated the question. She in turn continued to explain the modern equipment of the hospital. Finally he asked, "Are you a *capitalista?*"

Anita, whose boiling point is notably low, stopped at this and answered with some emotion: "If you are speaking of the doctors who leave their homes and their practices and give up their incomes to come here to Trujillo to teach your people and treat your sick without compensation; if you are talking about the nurses, technicians and others who for a full year will expose themselves voluntarily to the danger of sickness from diseases of climate, go to your mountains or work in your jungles much harder than they do at home; if you are thinking of all the people on the ship who make sacrifices because of their wish to help Peruanos and be their friends, then my answer is: Emphatically, YES, I AM A CAPITALISTA!"

The Peruvians broke into loud applause, and the man who

had asked the question beat a hasty retreat, vanishing at the end of the passageway.

LaVerne Fakkema persisted with awesome determination in the development of the barriada program. She was now receiving strong support from all our pediatricians, and in particular Dr. Jean Kohn, who instituted our first mass immunization program as an attention-getter to open up the Esperanza clinic. The physicians in Trujillo were deeply concerned over the people in the barriadas, and fearful that the clinics might not be continued after our departure. We tried to persuade them that running the clinics could and should be a medical-school function, with both students and instructors participating, much as in our own county hospitals.

While we were talking, LaVerne was doing. She visited with Señor Victor Burgos, "mayor" of Esperanza, and went straight to the point. We would need, she said, a place to work, to set up a clinic, to keep supplies. Señor Burgos responded in kind; he took LaVerne to a partially completed building already bearing the name *supermercado*. An enterprising citizen had begun the construction of the supermarket and then had run out of financing, or perhaps had had second thoughts about its success in this area of poverty and unemployment. In any case he had discontinued construction. There was no roof, but some walls had been built separating rooms or stalls from one another. LaVerne's imagination took over from there. She was able to envision an appointment desk in the sunlight at the end of the passageway, and specialty clinics where now were only three unfinished rooms. Sheets could be suspended from cross-bars so that two patients could be in each room simultaneously. Looking to the right of her imaginary desk, she spied a long stall with a low wall separating it from the open part of the market-to-be. Ideal for pediatrics, she thought; separated from the rest of the "rooms," and large enough to accommodate two pediatricians with the low wall separating the waiting line from the others. The remainder of the enclosure was simply one big open court with no electricity. All clinics would be held by day, so this did not matter. Trujillo's constant afternoon sun would provide ample light for the reflectors on the microscope and examining mirrors.

She quickly explained her ideas to Señor Burgos, and told him she must have volunteers to construct the benches and desks that would be required. Women of the barrio must make and launder the sheets needed for the clinics. Still another group would be needed to keep the clinic clean. Finally, at least one room must have a roof constructed over it and a door fitted with a lock so that certain equipment and drugs needed daily could be stored in the clinic with at least minimum safety. There was no water, sterile or otherwise, but for the time being this would have to be brought from the ship.

Señor Burgos quickly called a meeting of the Esperanza Association council, and LaVerne told the members of her plans and requirements. They could hardly contain themselves, so excited were they at this new adventure. LaVerne herself could not realize then how much she had advanced the concept of self-help among these people. They did not even have the funds to buy the wood for the crude desks and benches, so they literally foraged for it wherever it could be found. Some donated chairs from their already meager possessions. The supermarket owner would accept no rent, and agreed to put the roof over the room that required one. The women of the barriada sewed pieces of cloth together to make sheets of a crazy-quilt pattern.

In the town of Trujillo itself, the original attitude of incredulity was soon replaced by wonder, and finally infectious enthusiasm prevailed. Volunteers came forward to work in the clinic. Rosemary de Clusener, a German woman who had lived in Trujillo for seventeen years, offered to do anything she could and became a translator, nurse's aide and, above all, a friend. "Where have you been?" she would ask over and over. "This is the example Trujillo has needed. It will do more good than all the money, food, and roads. You have given these people attention and a chance to help themselves. You have given them the beginning of pride. You brought them hope!"

Jorge de Vinatea put out a call for volunteer physicians, and a few came forward to help. It seemed as if an entire community had been captured by a unique human experiment, and almost breathlessly awaited its outcome.

LaVerne succeeded in persuading the local authorities to give her two public health nurses to work in the project. In just one whirlwind effort, all the objectives of Project HOPE seemed to have jelled: self-help, partnership, and a response to Yankee initiative. All this was stimulated by the quiet girl from California.

Next on the schedule was getting the people of the entire barriada to come to the clinic. For the time being, no charge was to be made by the Esperanza Association fathers, and we agreed that this was wise. Even a token fee would have made the people suspicious.

Dr. Jean Kohn felt strongly that if we could attract the children to the clinic, the parents, some of whom had never received medical attention in their lives, would see the benefits. All parents, whether Peruvian, Indian, African, or Chinese, do love their children. She felt that a mass immunization program against the diseases that were crippling and killing these barriada children would do much to overcome any reluctance the citizens of Esperanza might have about attending the clinic. The Communists were saying that this was all a Yankee imperialist trick and that we were attempting to find deformities that had resulted from the fallout of our nuclear explosions so that we could experiment upon them. But these mothers, illiterate as they were, knew that the children of the better families lived longer than their own because of the

magic in the needles they received. They wanted the same for
their own youngsters, and Jean Kohn had heard their pleas
daily. So it was decided that this would be the opening
function of the clinic. Appointments could then be made for
future examinations at another time. Almost the entire staff of
the *Hope* volunteered, and it was only the disappointed who
had to remain on board to carry out their other chores.

The day the clinic opened, LaVerne, Jean Kohn, Barbara
Schwenk, our senior laboratory technician from Milwaukee,
and others loaded themselves into the Volkswagen bus and
headed for Esperanza, carrying all kinds of equipment and
alcohol, vaccine, sterile water, and adrenalin. They hoped to
meet their Peruvian counterparts at Esperanza, and openly
wondered whether they would show up. A further worry was
the patients: Would the clinic be well attended? As they
approached the barriada, it appeared deserted. The driver
turned off the road into a wide sandy street. Not a soul could
be seen. The Communists had convinced them after all. Then
they came to the street where the *supermercado*, now known
as the "Clínica Esperanza," was located. A roar went up from a
tremendous crowd that had been silently awaiting their arrival.
Shouts of "Hopie, Hopie, Hopie!" rang out, and hands reached
out to touch each of the staff members as they attempted to
reach the clinic. A group of cleanly scrubbed schoolchildren,
dressed in homemade white dresses, was grouped in front of
Señor Burgos, singing the song especially prepared for the
occasion. Many of the people wore shoes, a sure sign that
this was indeed a day of celebration. Señor Burgos spoke a few
words of friendship, and then the clinic was officially opened.
They were so proud of the makeshift furniture and the hanging sheets that Archie Golden, one of our pediatricians, actually cried. A cocky young man when he came with us, and
supercritical as so many physicians of his age are, he suddenly
realized at that moment what HOPE really meant. LaVerne

simply stood and looked, only the hint of a smile on her face, for she rarely revealed her emotions. But how proud she must have been!

One of the physicians, making his first visit to a barriada, muttered under his breath, as he saw the sick and needy mass, that they looked "like the breathing dead," and still another whispered, "My God, my God, what could we possibly do to deserve this?" as he and the others made their way through the large crowd gathered to welcome them.

These poorest of the poor were reaching out gently to touch them, rewarding the Americans with some of their rare smiles and many, many "thank yous." Quite a few were crying, and some were waving homemade American flags.

The HOPE staffers, now rapidly inoculating child after child against typhoid, whooping cough, tetanus, poliomyelitis, and the like, were committed to their mission. Only three were pediatricians; the others were surgeons, neurosurgeons, obstetricians, men who had not performed such tasks as this in years. Yet here they were, leading American specialists, working in the sand and desert sun of a coastal barriada in Peru. Their concentration amply demonstrated their dedication to the task before them. "Gringo" would never again be a term of derision in Trujillo, but rather one of praise and warmth. The people had begun to know North Americans as they really are, rather than as inventions of some politician.

The next day, almost as if by magic, the *Yanqui, go home* signs began to disappear. The *Comunismo sí, Yanqui no* slogans were washed from the walls of Trujillo. This could not have happened a moment too soon, for trouble was in the offing. A strong anchor was to be needed—sooner than we had ever anticipated.

But even as the danger signs were coming down in Trujillo, in Lima storm signals were being hoisted. The presidential election campaign in Peru reached its climax in June; it never really seemed to catch fire despite the intense rivalry between candidates. Foreign diplomats seemed more concerned over the outcome than the Peruvians themselves. Support was about equally divided among the three political leaders: Odria on the right, Belaunde in the center, and Haya de la Torre on the left. It was almost certain that no candidate would be successful in obtaining the more than one-third majority required by the Peruvian constitution to elect a President.

Haya de la Torre, a reformed Communist, was the leader of the Aprista Party, and had the support of the Castroites. The Apristas themselves are not Communist, but their political ideals are definitely far to the left. Haya was running on a ticket of "instant reform and instant seizure," and boasted of having the support of the United States official family. Despite repeated denials of United States interference in the campaign on Haya's behalf, the Peruvians generally accepted Haya's boast as true. Unfortunately, some of our officials were quoted as having said that "Haya was the only candidate who was really concerned for the people." This allegation swept Lima, driving many protest votes to Odria and thus ensuring a three-way dead heat. True or not, we North Americans know that one of our greatest faults is talking too much to small groups "in confidence." Later we find ourselves thoroughly surprised at being misquoted or quoted at all.

The importance of the election campaign to HOPE was that we were in Trujillo, seat of the Aprista Party, and the town Haya liked to call his real home, although in fact the latter was some miles away. There was also heavy Communist influence in the area, the further irritant of extensive North American business holdings surrounding the town, and the history of Trujillo itself. It was here that some twenty years earlier, Haya de la Torre, then an avowed Communist, had led an abortive uprising against the government. Temporarily successful, his forces had captured some military officers (the number varies from a few up to the hundreds, depending upon who is telling the story) and "put them to the wall." The military have never forgotten the incident, and were determined to keep Haya from leading the government. They professed a sincere fear that under Haya the nation would become another Cuba. There is no rule of thumb that should govern the judgment passed on military leaders in Latin America. Frequently they are a stabilizing force in nations seeking too radical a change too quickly. Each must be judged on his own merits.

We, as Norteamericanos, were therefore in a strange position. Haya claimed the support of our government for his policy of instant change, and his followers quoted North American politicians to prove it. We of HOPE were committed to our own policy of slow and steady progress; President Kennedy himself, in initiating the Alliance, had said this was only a beginning. This was not, however, sufficient to quiet the howls of the instant reformers.

Marty Kohn, our acting chief of staff, and I discussed the impending crisis, and arrived at several decisions. First, regardless of the outcome of the election and its aftermath, the *Hope* would remain on station and its staff continue to carry out its mission. We would lift anchor only in the event of a direct attack on our personnel or a serious danger to the safety of the vessel. After all, events of recent weeks had convinced us that we enjoyed the confidence and friendship of the people in the area.

My oldest son, Bill, Jr., then almost seventeen, was on board, having come to Peru with a classmate, Jeff Steele, to work as summer volunteers in the barriadas. We discussed with him the potential dangers of the situation and suggested that he carry on as usual—although he must recognize that there could be trouble. It was a question that only he could decide: to remain as a symbol of my confidence in the people, and risk a possible "hostage" kidnaping should a revolution begin, or journey to Lima with the rest of the family. He chose to remain in Trujillo, and I was very proud of him.

As for myself, I would go to Casa Hope in Lima so as to be available to whatever government came into power. Fernando Cabieses had already insisted that I move my family there. Cabby was worried, and since he did not frighten easily I felt that his advice should be followed. He added that should trouble come, all phone communications with Trujillo would be cut off and that we had better be prepared to communicate with the ship via ham radio. Bernardo Batievsky, one of the finest friends Hope ever had in Peru, provided the Lima end of the communications system, and placed a car and chauffeur at our disposal.

As the voting began and returns started to come in, the anticipated horse race began. There were no computers, no television seers to assure the outcome, so the counting went on for days. Tension mounted, and cries of "fraud" went up from every side. If any candidate went into the lead, almost by magic another district would report in as counterbalance. It reminded me of late returns from "safe" wards in some of our own urban areas at home.

Then rumors of wheeling and dealing began, and it became apparent that right was going to merge with left, pushing Haya into the executive mansion. Belaunde prudently departed for Arequipa, well to the south, and the rumbling of tanks and troops could be heard in the streets. We remained at Casa Hope in a state of complete confusion, hearing rumors of uprisings in the North and riots in Cuzco. Our Spanish, bad enough at best, deserted us completely as we tried to follow the overanxious commentators on television. When my youngest son, Tommy, went out the front door and reported a tank on our corner, we had the feeling that a climax was soon to come.

Haya was forging into the lead, although still a few tenths short of a majority, and the military determined to make its move before it was too late. At about 10:00 P.M. on the climactic evening in July, our telephone, which had not rung for days, came alive. When I answered, a man who did not wish to be identified advised me he was calling on behalf of the still incumbent President Prado. He stated that the President was quite well but would likely be arrested that night. The President wished me to be assured that no matter what happened, it was his desire that the *Hope* remain at work in Trujillo, for it had made a real impression on the people. If we moved, it would result in rioting, with the blame laid unjustly at someone's door. The caller then rang off.

We watched the television all evening, and finally heard the broadcast stating that the military had indeed taken power "to save the republic." President Prado, unharmed, had been placed in protective custody, and eventually wound up on the Riviera. At about 2:00 A.M., the phone rang once again. On this occasion the unidentified voice (I suspect it was the same one) from the Palace, now speaking on behalf of Pérez Godoy, president of the Military Junta, repeated virtually his same plea made four hours earlier. Added to this was the "absolute guarantee" of protection for the ship and all her personnel. Cabby came by shortly afterward and recommended that we do nothing till morning. He said that all the streets were clear and that the military seemed in control, with no evidence of any serious violence.

At seven the same morning, I immediately went to the American Embassy, where lights had burned all night. The ambassador had just recommended the severing of diplomatic relations between our two countries as a symbol of protest against military takeover. This could mean the cessation of almost all financial and other aid from the United States, and could precipitate the very situation in Peru which the military had seized power to prevent. The position of the United States was explained to me as being based on the premise that we could not recognize a government that was not constitutionally elected. The military leaders of Peru protested that they were pro-American and that our policy in this regard had a history of inconsistency. Besides, they asked, how could a fraudulent election be constitutional? Shortly thereafter, our government took the position that any humanitarian programs in which it was engaged should be continued. In effect, therefore, it was a break in relations, yet not a complete one. As a nongovernment effort, we were not affected by the decision one way or another. Certainly, however, we would not do anything contrary to the best interests of the United States.

While all this was taking place in Lima, word of the military takeover had been flashed all over the country. Military commanders were put in charge of all cities and provinces. In Trujillo, because serious trouble was expected the garrison had been increased and the town placed under the command of General Rodríguez Razzetto. During the night many people had journeyed to the port of Salaverry; when dawn broke, the crowd had swelled to several hundred, and the stretch of water between ship and shore looked awfully good. There was no way of telling what the people were thinking.

At almost the same moment that I was in the Embassy in Lima, General Razzetto and a group of heavily armed aides boarded the *Hope* in Trujillo. They came in peace, and assured Dr. Kohn that the ship and its personnel would be guaranteed every safety. They made the same plea to him that had been made to me twice the previous evening: "Please do not move the ship. If you do, it will be interpreted as a reprisal against the military government, and will be the signal for bloodletting in the streets of Trujillo." The first twenty-four hours following such a seizure of power is always critical. The first act of violence can lead to thousands of casualties that can cripple a nation.

Marty made the right decision. He assured General Rodríguez Razzetto that he would carry on as usual unless he heard to the contrary from us in Lima. General Razzetto was most grateful, and spent most of the next year demonstrating this gratitude in a spirit of complete cooperation with our mission.

This is not to say that there were not anxious moments or even some riots. But a miracle did happen. Not a single Peruvian was killed by either side in that first twenty-four hours. The Military Junta promised free elections in one year (a promise they kept), and exercised admirable restraint otherwise. In the early days following the takeover, we would install ourselves in the bar of the famous Hotel Bolívar at six o'clock so that we could watch the demonstration staged there nightly. Rarely was anyone hurt, but each evening an ancient *colectivo* would be burned, and the crowds would mill about and shove so that the North American news photographers could obtain the appropriate pictures. The soldiers stood aside benevolently until the demonstration was ended, and would then send the crowd on its way. The next day we would buy the American newspapers and read of the violent demonstrations that were endangering us.

The truth was that except for a frustrated Communist minority, the people of Lima were almost apathetic. The Junta takeover had been expected, and no one was surprised. There was some resentment against America's breaking diplomatic relations, but almost as much tolerant amusement at the action. The chief concern was how long it would take for our country to recognize the new government. The Peruvians literally adored President Kennedy, and though they felt he had followed bad advice, they did not identify him at all with the diplomatic break. In short, it was a curious revolution.

There was almost a sense of relief that the election no one could win was deferred for another year. In the outlying districts there were student strikes and the schools were closed for a brief period. In Trujillo the university went on strike, but the medical students never missed a day on the *Hope*. There were transportation strikes in Trujillo and Salaverry, but the *Hope* launches, buses, and other vehicles kept going as usual. The barriada program continued without interruption: not a clinic was missed, nor was a patient lost.

[10]

While politicians were fighting over the future of Peru, the people of Trujillo, together with those aboard the S.S. *Hope*, were doing something constructive about it. Almost oblivious to the tensions, Archbishop Pérez Silva gathered together two committees made up of the local ladies of position and substance in answer to a call for help from us of the *Hope*.

The nurse auxiliary training program was about to begin to teach trainees a skill that would benefit the entire community. Our trainees were drawn primarily from the poorer families, and would have to be paid something since, in leaving other occupations, the meager contributions they made to their parents and families would be gone. The bishop had pledged that he would organize a men's committee to obtain funds, but what of uniforms, shoes, transportation, and interpreters? This was to be the job for the women of Trujillo.

As at all meetings, there was too much noise and too little decided until a small bell tinkled, our alert to get down to business. If material were bought and the girls asked to make their own clothes, there would be delays and lack of uniformity; a quick decision was made to buy the thirty or more sets of uniforms required per group. Shoes of the same style and color would be provided for those who needed them. Car pools would bring to work those not living on the ship, for the parents of some young ladies felt that it would not be proper for them to live "unchaperoned." Committees of interpreters were organized for duty on the ship, in the clinics and wards at Belén Hospital and in the barriadas. While there was the expected attrition that one finds in all volunteer groups, women like Tenny Roselle, Marcella de Ganoza, and Rosemary de Clusener never missed a day or failed in an assigned task.

It was during this same period that Ron Turnbow, a dairy engineer contributed to us for a year by the Foremost Dairies, began his daily "milk run" in the barriadas, assisted by summer student volunteers. Utilizing a Coca-Cola truck donated by the local distributor, Ron, Bill, Jr., and the Barton boys, Tom and Paul, from Albany, New York, would leave for the barriadas and other points every afternoon about half past two. The boys started to haul the milk up some five decks from the *Hope's* already famous Iron Cow shortly after lunch. Then it was wrestled down the gangway and onto the launch, to be greeted by Othello's excited bark. Although it is doubtful that Othello suffered from protein deficiency, he always managed to persuade the crew to give him his pint. From the dock the truck took off in a cloud of dust for Esperanza. Then, in words written by another observer, "the daily tug at the heartstrings began":

They start running, barefooted through the heavy desert sands, as the first roar of the truck engine splits the quiet of the barriada. As they run, their shouts of Opey, Opey [Hopie, Hopie], or Leche, Leche, carry a note of joyous anticipation.

These are the children of the barriada. Indian children for the most part, dressed in rags, shod—if at all—in sandals that have passed from one generation to another. Many of them are malnourished; and yet ironically they often appear fat and healthy.

But behind the façade of superficial health linger the old killers: tuberculosis, smallpox, the fevers; and the maimers: rickets, polio, cleft palates, and incipient starvation. . . . The routine as established by Ron Turnbow never varies. It has to be the same, for here there is an atmosphere of desperation.

First, the children in the schools must get their one-third-quart ration per student. When this is done, general distribution to the younger children, expectant mothers, babies, and old people.

Set up a table—form a line—pass out the milk cartons, only one to a person. Turnbow, his crew, and the teachers attempt to maintain order. But soon the discipline breaks down, and the wave of children crush in on nurse Carolyn Stoll, who is this day passing out the milk.

There is no panic, certainly no violence. Determination, yes. Just to be one of those who does not come away empty-handed. The fact is cruel and unavoidable—there is *never* enough milk to go around.

At they near the end of the allotment for this stop, Miss Stoll, Turnbow, and the others effect a strategic withdrawal to the truck, at the same time thrusting the last cartons of milk into the outstretched hands of the mothers and children.

Quickly now: into the waiting truck—first gear—second gear—while in the back, they are still passing out cartons. As the truck rumbles off the older boys keep pace with the heavily laden vehicle as it digs through the shifting sand. Some try to catch a ride on the tailgate. The bribe of another carton of milk encourages them to let go, and clutching their precious cargo, they drop unhurt and triumphant into the warm soft sand.

This performance was repeated daily as a kind of game—a serious one—in the fight against disease. Between seven thousand and eight thousand cartons of milk were delivered weekly, to many the first they had ever seen. And the milk was made from the sea some five decks down in the *Hope*, thousands of gallons of seawater were pumped into evaporating tanks daily, desalted, purified, then combined with milk properties. The surplus milk solids came from the government, other anhydrous fats and butter from American dairy contributors, and the cartons made by a machine donated by still other American industries. It is the best kind of package deal from a democracy: goodwill and protein simultaneously.

Milk distribution was far from the only activity at the

barriada clinics. Their confidence won, the lines of patients daily grew longer and we appealed to Señor Burgos for laborers to enlarge the clinic by finishing two more examination spaces. Every type of patient came in. The hacking coughs of tuberculosis were everywhere. Shoeless children came infested with hookworm; since the parasite penetrated through bare feet there could be no cure unless shoes followed the treatment. Child after child with the long residual effects of severe polio dragged shriveled limbs to the clinic, hoping for a miracle. Infections of the skin, which could have been prevented earlier or cured with a little soap and water, were now major infections and abscesses, many requiring hospitalization. Cleft lips and cleft palates, the result of frequent births in a malnourished atmosphere, were everywhere. Herb Bloom, our oral surgeon, often remarked that you could walk down the sandy street of any barriada and pick out a dozen. In the clinic we saw only those who were intelligent enough to seek help. The elderly came out of curiosity; they wanted to see what a doctor looked like and what he did. A bottle of medicine or a package of vitamins was a treasure, the first medication most of them had ever had.

Though the long lines continued to lengthen, the patients always waited quietly, no pushing or shoving, no complaining. They came dressed in their Sunday best, and those that had shoes wore them. They were always scrubbed so clean one could not but wonder at the achievement, since their homes were floored with mud and their only water came from whatever stream they could find.

I best remember Archie Golden, Anne Watkins, and our other pediatricians who each day patiently examined sixty or seventy youngsters. At first their Spanish was hesitant and halting, but day by day the interpreters became less necessary and the patient-load heavier. Students and Peruvian physicians began to join us regularly as the summer wore on, and Archie,

who had been so cocky when he arrived, gradually learned to
be patient, and grew to understand and love the people. If
anyone had told him during those early August days that he
was to spend three years in Trujillo, Archie would have told
him to see his psychiatrist. But this is exactly what was to
happen.

In Belén Hospital, our nurses and physicians began to work
in the wards and—with some reluctance—in the operating
rooms. Mary Damuth was our first pioneer in the surgical ward
at Belén, and began by teaching her nurses to scrub the floors
and the walls. With her Spanish already reasonably fluent, she
gained a ready acceptance. Little by little she persuaded and
cajoled, and finally was given a demonstration ward of eight
beds all her own. Here, assisted by her Peruvian students, she
developed a demonstration center that was to be the model for
change in the entire hospital. Dr. Alfredo Acuña, our early
nemesis and later good friend, the chief of surgery at Belén,
was the first to acknowledge the success of Mary's efforts. He
proudly took all visitors to "his ward" to demonstrate how well
the collaboration with HOPE was working.

We were all learning to understand one another. Dr. Acuña
obviously felt that the way to make us feel welcome was to
have the hospital serve us luncheon in our own private room.
This was the last thing we were looking for, but we belatedly
recognized that it was his beginning gesture of friendship. We,
like all gringos, naturally wanted to begin by tearing up his
operating rooms, putting in a complete new system, changing
his habits of twenty-five years and, in effect, unintentionally
humiliating him before his entire staff. He had waited a lifetime for help, didn't believe it when it came, trusted it less,
and we wanted to package it and deliver it overnight.

After months of sparring, it became obvious that our surgeons were going to have to begin by operating in the Belén
operating rooms as they were, almost in an effort to demon-

strate that it could not and should not be done. Our nurses
protested violently; if we persisted in this plan, they said, all
the stress on good nursing techniques already demonstrated
would go down the drain. But there seemed no choice if we
were seeking to make a permanent impact in Trujillo, for
although many surgeons and students were working on the
ship, Dr. Acuña was still the Dean of Surgery in Trujillo. If we
did not win him over, the chance of lasting improvement in
medicine in that city was all but lost. Some of our girls never
did understand how we could "compromise" our principles.
But "compromise" them we did, and the "villains" were some
of the finest surgeons in America, who had the humility to
recognize that Alfredo Acuña was master of his own house—
and it was in this house that we must work in order to win our
point.

Dr. Acuña felt that we could not properly advise, suggest, or
criticize until we worked in the same atmosphere in which he
did. He was concerned that if all the surgeons of his staff
worked on the *Hope,* without our surgeons working in Belén,
no permanent good could be accomplished. There was a
wisdom in this. The change, to be permanent, had to be at
Belén. Alfredo was aware of certain deficiencies, and was
attempting to obtain funds from the Beneficencia, the group of
laymen who controlled hospital finances, for new operating
rooms at Belén. In this oblique fashion he was enlisting our
aid, without sacrificing pride or dignity in saying so. His
appeal for our understanding was, in effect, the same appeal
that we were making to our nurses for theirs. The decision was
made to go ahead, and with much strained feeling among our
own staff, the experiment commenced.

A more difficult two months cannot be imagined. Our surgeons agreed to work at Belén provided that one of our
anesthetists could teach and administer anesthesia while they
worked, and with the further condition that one of our own

surgical nursing supervisors be placed in Belén for a trial two-month period. Nurse Cecelia Mooney, a girl strong of mind and body, was selected for the latter post. A perfectionist in her own right, she was supervising operating rooms in which sterile technique was an impossibility. Autoclaves were not being used; neither nurses nor physicians could properly prepare for surgery with the existing facilities. Operating-room gowns were so short in the sleeves that inches of hairy arms showed between the top of the gloves and the bottom of the gown sleeves, defeating every purpose of preoperative preparation. Instruments were dull and not properly sterilized. The wonder was that anyone survived. The day that Mayfield Harris, our orthopedic surgeon, had to operate with two sets of Kelly clamps hanging from his sleeves so as to keep them from flapping during surgery was almost the last straw. Each time he moved his arms the hemostats would clang together like a warning bell. Mooney seethed and threatened to resign every day. What Mooney did not know was that Alfredo Acuña knew all these deficiencies well. Until we had arrived, he had almost given up any hope of getting positive action on his requests from the Beneficencia. He did not know us well enough to take us into his confidence, but he was using us for a purpose: a dramatic but properly worded appeal from us might just embarrass these holders of the purse strings into helping him solve his problem.

I believe that the report submitted after a two-month trial period by Dr. Charles Geraci, the acting chief of our surgical staff, was a masterpiece in soft understatement, but quite effective enough to achieve Dr. Acuña's objective. It is included in part here, for it not only tells the story of Belén, but in its manner of presentation demonstrates why HOPE succeeds where so many others have failed. This report was accompanied by a letter stating that if certain of these steps were not undertaken immediately, we could no longer work in Belén:

s.s. *Hope* at SALAVERRY, PERU

REPORT OF HOPE ACTIVITIES AND OPERATIONS
AT BELÉN HOSPITAL

Submitted by

CHARLES L. GERACI, M.D.
Chief of Surgery
Chief of Staff

DEAR DOCTORS:

This report is written to you in behalf of the surgical staff at
Belén Hospital and the surgical staff of the S.S. *Hope*. The
doctors and nurses of the S.S. *Hope* have been working in the
surgical department of Belén Hospital for approximately two
months, and we must report that we have been greatly encouraged by the spirit of cooperation and friendliness with which
we have been received. Through our close associations with
our surgical counterparts at Belén Hospital and in the Escuela
de Medicina, we have become closely involved in the problems
the hospital and its surgical department faces in the areas of
surgery. In our attempts to bring to the surgeons of Trujillo the
benefits of the most modern surgical techniques, we have, from
time to time, made various suggestions which have been very
well received. I am sure you understand that we are not here
in Trujillo merely to perform operations and to treat patients,
but rather to try to help the doctors and the people of Trujillo
in their attempts to bring ever better and better medicine to
their area, even as we make those attempts in our own country.
Therefore we feel it is important to demonstrate our surgical
techniques and our methods of treatment in a manner as similar to that of the United States as it is possible to accomplish at
Belén Hospital. . . . I am sure that you can understand that
we have certain standards which we have to meet in our surgical treatments and that to lower our standards would not be in
the best interests of the doctors at Belén Hospital. We would
like, therefore, to make a few suggestions to the Beneficencia
Society and to the surgeons of Belén Hospital, none of which
would involve the expenditure of large amounts of money but
would make the practice of surgery at Belén more convenient,

pleasant, and safe. Our suggestions and recommendations are as follows:

OPERATING-ROOM AREAS

It is our first observation concerning the operating room that surgical instruments and equipment are not truly being sterilized, and we feel this constitutes some danger to any operating room. Surgical instruments and packs are, at the present time, being sterilized in a hot oven for approximately ten minutes. The linens are placed in the hot oven wet, and come out of the oven quite damp. It is a well known fact that sterilization in a hot oven requires 8 to 12 hours, and the short period of time used at Belén Hospital we do not consider adequate. There is, however, an autoclave present in the laundry which can be put to excellent use in the autoclaving of surgical packs. At this time, the autoclave does not function completely well and we do not recommend that it be used under the present conditions.

We do recommend that the representative from the American Sterilizer Company in Lima be asked to come to the hospital immediately for the purpose of servicing the autoclave so that it can be made to function completely properly. At the present time the surgeons of the S.S. *Hope* do bring with them all of their own sterilized equipment when they perform surgery at Belén, and because of the great amount of equipment necessary for this, it is possible for us to manage only one operation daily. As soon as the autoclave is activated and functioning properly, however, it will be possible for us then to use the sterilized packs from your hospital and then we could help, be present at, or perform two or several operations each day. At the present time the autoclave is used only in the morning because there is no provision for the use of steam for the autoclave in the afternoon. However, all of the operating is done in the morning and it would be necessary for preparation of sterile packs for the next day to have the autoclave functioning in the afternoon. This is an absolute necessity.

In order to be properly prepared for several operations a day, it would be necessary to obtain sufficient double-thickness operating sheets and drapes of proper size, which are not presently in use at Belén, in order that the packs could be autoclaved and ready ahead of time. Our measurements and specifications for all of our packs and sheets were given to the operating room at the hospital at one time and some sheets were actually made up, but they were then later distributed to the wards, and are not available to the operating room. We would be most happy to give you once again the measurements for our drapes and sheets, and would recommend that they be stamped or in some other way identified as belonging solely to the operating room.

We have noted that the surgical gowns used in the operating room are tied at the wrists with tie straps, and the sleeves are often open well up the arm. We feel that this completely destroys the value of the use of gloves in the operating room as the bare arm above the glove is no better than a naked hand. It is our recommendation that all surgical gowns in the operating area be supplied with an elastic type of cuff which we would be most happy to describe and demonstrate to you.

There has been improvement in the supply of brushes for surgical scrubbing, but we do feel that enough sterile brushes should be supplied for scrubbing so that no doctor must use someone else's discarded brush to prepare his hands for surgery. In addition, any form of liquid soap from a wall dispenser is superior to the use of bar soap for the scrubbing of hands. We have supplied for the operating room two wall soap dispensers and a small supply of antiseptic detergent, but liquid soap is really not expensive and could be used in as satisfactory a manner as the more expensive detergents as long as the surgeons scrub their hands for ten minutes. The scrubbing of the hands with any good soap for ten minutes is as cleansing as scrubbing the hands with a powerful germicide for only a few minutes. In this connection, it is our recommendation that the area of the surgeons' scrub sinks be supplied with a wall clock in order to time the surgical scrubs. It is our observation that there are not adequate suction machines in all the operating rooms, and we feel that this is extremely important in the management of anesthetized patients. We certainly recommend that a small suction machine be obtained for every operating room in the hospital in order that this could be used both during surgery and for the cleansing of the patient's bronchial passages during and after the operation.

In addition, we think that there should be one suction machine on each surgical ward.

We are aware that the new operating room is being prepared to facilitate the handling of the very many surgical patients which you have at Belén. We are very much in agreement with your plans, as we feel that you badly need these new operating rooms. We would like to offer our services to you, if you wish them, in helping you to set up the operating room. In addition to this, if you wish it, we will be happy to supply personnel for using one operating room daily for the conduct of surgical operations. The only request we have, however, is that at all times we operate with Peruvian doctors, our anesthetists work with Peruvian anesthetists or trainees, and our nurses work with your auxiliaries or trainees. This last request is because we do not feel we are here mainly to perform operations, but to impart what knowledge we have to give, and we can do that only if there is someone present to receive it.

The following constitutes our suggestions and recommendations for the wards:

WARD AREAS

Our first and most major recommendation is that one ward on the male service and one ward on the female service should be set aside for the intensive care of postoperative patients. This one room should be arranged and equipped to care for all of the postoperative surgical patients during the first one to three days after their operations, which is the most critical period. Should you so desire, we would be most happy to assist in any way we could in the setting up of such a postoperative intensive care ward.

We feel that it is important that the surgeon visit all the postoperative patients on the day of surgery before he leaves the hospital. This is true because the first few hours are the most critical hours in the evolution of a postoperative patient, and no one can judge the evolution as well as the surgeon himself.

We believe that there should be a small water sterilizer present on each ward in order to sterilize needles, syringes, and instruments properly.

It is our recommendation that small sterile pans with a few

sterile instruments be kept on each ward. At the present it is practically impossible to do a dressing on the wards in the afternoon or evening, as it is necessary to send to the operating room for the instruments.

NURSING SUGGESTIONS

Our nurses, who have been working in the hospital for the past two months, have felt that they could make numerous recommendations for the more efficient functioning of the wards, and they have outlined just a few of these suggestions:

The appointment of a head nurse for each ward.

There should be one professional nurse on every shift, or at least one as a nursing supervisor.

It is imperative that there be a nursing report given between nursing shifts. At the present time no report is being given, and a nurse coming on the shift does not know what has happened to the patients during the previous shift.

There should be a written ward report for the supervisor from the nurses on every shift.

We observe that there have been no nursing notes made on the patients' charts. This makes it impossible to tell from looking at a patient's chart exactly what his evolution has been. We suggest that nursing notes be kept on all patients' charts, and we would be most happy to demonstrate samples of our charts in order to help the nursing staff familiarize themselves with this type of form.

We would like to recommend that the physicians make written postoperative orders on all patients leaving the operating room, as we think that this is one of the most important functions of the surgeon and of the patient's chart.

We would like to recommend that there be one nurse or auxiliary for the postoperative care of the surgical patients on their day of surgery. If an intensive-care unit were set up in each ward, the one nurse could take care of all the surgical patients in that one ward.

There should be a postoperative care sheet for every postoperative patient. Our nurses on the ward have made up postoperative care sheets for all of our patients operated at Belén, and we think they have been favorably received.

It is our suggestion that a nurse should travel with all patients coming from the operating room to the ward.

We would like to recommend also that there be thermometers, at least 24 for a 66-bed unit, in order to facilitate the taking of temperatures.

At the present time, the doctors give daily orders on the patients. We feel that this is superfluous and should not be necessary. We believe that doctors' orders written on the charts should stand until they are changed or discontinued. This would free some of the doctor's time so that he could do more important treatments. Many of the orders written for patients, such as for vitamins, are practically always given for all patients who are able to eat. We feel that, rather than write such orders daily, a simple arrangement would be to make standing orders so that all patients receive them unless there are orders to the contrary.

We would like to recommend that the nursing staff on the wards be assigned certain patients because we feel that only in this way can the responsibility for the care of the patients be localized.

Our nurses have made much more complete reports and recommendations to us which, if you are agreeable, we can pass on to you at any time you desire.

It is our most fervent hope that the members of the Beneficencia Society and the surgeons of the Belén Hospital do not misunderstand the sincerity with which we make these recommendations. We want to be able to feel that when the S.S. *Hope* leaves Trujillo we have made it possible for the doctors of the Belén Hospital to improve the stature of their medical and surgical care and to feel that both we and you have done a good job in your hospital. We are extremely grateful for the opportunities we have had to associate with you and with the doctors of Trujillo; we hope we can continue forward in an atmosphere of mutual trust, confidence, and friendliness such as we have come to know here in Trujillo.

We are making these suggestions to you in writing because we hope they will assume more importance after having been written and because we feel that, in order to make the further progress which I know you want for your hospital, you must know where to begin and we, as outsiders, may be able to bring a fresh, unbiased viewpoint to you. We feel that we have advanced about as far as we can go for the present time until some of your contemplated changes are made. The simple repairing of the autoclave, arranging for it to function throughout the entire day, and the procurement of sufficient instruments and pack materials would allow both you and us to make a tremendous step forward in the surgical care of the people of Trujillo.

Respectfully submitted,
CHARLES L. GERACI, M.D.
Chief of Staff
Chief of Surgery

Dr. Alfredo Acuña was indeed a wise man, of great restraint. The changes were made.

[11]

Fall brought little change to the climate of Salaverry, since weather remains the same throughout the year, with a little less fog in the morning as August fades into September. The seasons are actually reversed, with our summer the Peruvian winter, and our winter season their summer. The cultural differences sometimes were as pronounced as this reversal of seasons, but we were all learning to adapt easily.

Hardly a day passed that one of our nurses would not find one of the patient's visitors in the ward shower. The idea of turning a handle and having hot water come out was almost too much for the mestizos to resist. When trapped in the shower, they would smile, shake their heads, and chatter their apologies in Quechua, their Indian language, instead of the Spanish they knew we understood. Helplessly our girls would simply say "Sí, sí," and hurriedly evacuate them. One afternoon, on the women's ward there were two discharges, yet at the change of the nursing shift the nurse coming on duty noticed that all her beds were filled, although the record showed no new admissions. Sure enough, two visitors had helped themselves to the clean pajamas laid upon the pillows, taken off their clothes, and climbed into the beds. It was the first opportunity either of them had ever had to sleep on anything but the hard ground, and they took advantage of it. Incidents such as these could only be handled with good humor, for the people were basically so gentle and kind. How could we help but laugh with them when they were caught?

While water was plentiful, from time to time we did run out of essential supplies, mainly because staff and crew found the people irresistible. With thousands upon thousands of supply items in a hospital of this size, who would have ever dreamed that we would run out of safety pins? Nicholas Craw, our logistics chief, will never be forgiven. Who ever heard of holding on babies' diapers with Scotch tape? It didn't work, and the linen in the pediatric ward took a terrible beating. Sheets were another item that suddenly were in short supply. We found, through the investigation of our quartermaster, that members of the crew were wrapping clean sheets around their waists and chests as they left the ship so that presents could be given to the ladies of Salaverry and Trujillo. While believing wholeheartedly in people-to-people relationships, we did feel this was going a bit far, and put a stop to it.

Marvin Garrison, our chief steward, also found that "sheets" of beefsteak were leaving the ship in the same fashion. Men would pilfer the steak and wrap it in bed linen tied around their waistlines. The only ingredient we weren't supplying for an evening of sport was the bottle of wine, and this was doubtless added on the mainland. One can at least take the charitable approach and conclude that the ladies of Salaverry were interested in improving their protein intake.

As in Indonesia, we were again challenged to a game of basketball by the university team. Some of our rotators, flushed with the memories of our success in the islands against teams averaging about five foot six in height, welcomed the challenge. They felt the honor of the *Hope* must be defended even though the age of our team would average approximately forty-six, a figure very close to our average player's girth of waistline. When they reached the field of combat, and were confronted with a lithe team averaging well over six feet in height, they realized, perhaps for the first time, that Peruvian young men stand tall. The details are too painful, but after the Trujillo Tigers rolled up fifty points, our team, now and forever known as the "Hapless Hopies," withdrew from the court in favor of our summer student volunteers. Although they did somewhat better, we were still soundly thrashed to the good-humored delight of a large audience.

By this time the ship's staff had been welded into a closely knit family. One of the standard routines on board is for the veterans (girls who return for a second or third voyage) to move into somewhat more comfortable quarters by virtue of seniority. Everyone starts out in a cabin for four, moving eventually to one for three, two, or to that treasured part of the boatdeck where they may have a room by themselves. It is all done good-naturedly, and the staff themselves give names to different parts of the ship so that before long everyone knows where to find the others. The worst accommodations, but those for which there is a waiting list, are the quarters of our rotating physicians—some of American Medicine's Finest. The majority of them live "barracks fashion" in one area, with twenty-three to one room. We thought that certain men in older age groups, or men with veteran status, should be given preferential treatment when possible. But "The Jungle," as it is called, turned out to be a favorite of the men, and the waiting list was drawn up in protest. Student volunteers, who lived in similarly crowded circumstances, were not to be outdone, and labeled their quarters "The Junior Jungle."

The girls in the four bed cabins, called "The Barriadas," wrote a song to the tune of "Ta-ra-ra Boom-de-ay" which they sang to the girls on the more luxurious boatdeck. It ended: "We love you, that is true; we're just not as clean as you," in reference to the extra showers available to the girls on the boatdeck.

There were other experiences on board that could certainly

never be celebrated in song and satire. Ethel Black, our admissions secretary, once wrote this description of the mother of a little boy who later died of meningitis:

When she first came in, she was sitting on the bench outside of our Admissions Office. I tried to talk to her but couldn't understand anything she said (some of these people speak a slight mixture of Quechua and Spanish) so I left her. Dr. Kohn came along and said, "You're going to take care of that mother, aren't you?"

She looked so old that I never dreamed she was the mother, not that her face was lined actually, but it had something to do with the texture of the skin and the expression on her face—a portrait of the ages. She had a scar on one side of her mouth; her hair was dark and hung in two braids down her back. She was dressed in several long skirts and over the top of the skirts she wore "something," a dark, faded, drab, blue heavy material. You couldn't call it a poncho and you couldn't call it an overdress. Well, it was just there. Her shoes were old and battered and worn; and when she sat, she didn't sit in the fidgety way as we would do, rather she waited resigned and peaceful, while eternity flowed around her. As someone said, it expressed hundreds of years of "waiting." Each day she just sat there, never changing, while the staff fought to save the baby's life. I wanted so to get her picture, but did not have the courage to intrude. The baby worsened and finally died. The day of the child's death, she gathered enough courage to come into my office, making no noise or furor, just tears running slowly down her cheeks. All she said was "esposo, esposo." She wanted her husband, but no one knew where he was. He was working somewhere in the area but didn't know his child had been ill. The pathos of this simple request made her seem so alone in her misery, I had to turn away. Some of our nurses went into town to find him and by nightfall he arrived at the ship. They left together in the same poignant scene so familiar to all of us in medicine anywhere in the world. A comfort to one another, a filling of the other's emptiness. No, my friend, life isn't cheap anywhere.

Another sad experience that Ethel cannot forget occurred the day that Nancy Campion asked her and Mary Damuth to take a father and his dead baby home:

The quartermaster cleared the deck leading to the gangway so that we could get Papa and his baby off with some semblance of dignity. The baby had been brought up from the Intensive Care Unit wrapped in a sheet, and Papa was carrying it in his arms. . . . When we reached the new dock, we had to fight our way through the crowd . . . pushing forward in its eagerness to board the launch we had just left. . . . But then they were unaware of our sad cargo, else they would have made a path for us.

We took the old jeep and drove through Trujillo to the barriada. Papa directed us off the main road, through alleyways and narrow little byways that had nothing to make them look like streets or roads, simply more potholes in the middle than on the pedestrian paths. Occasionally we saw a small family of pigs tied up in a front yard; in others a goat was tethered and we knew some fortunate family was getting milk.

Finally he told us to stop in front of one house. I jumped down from one side of the jeep and Papa handed me the motionless bundle. It was a strange feeling, to hold a small child, so still, so lifeless, so dead. When he was out of the jeep, I quickly handed him the baby back. He tapped on the door and we entered. There were three rooms divided by very dirty paper-thin walls. At one time they must have had plaster on them, but now it was chipped and hanging. There were windows cut in the sides of the house, but no glass filled the frames. Dirty white cloths hung from the frames in an effort to curtain their privacy. A little girl with a running nose and a dirty face backed out of the room as we entered. Several other youngsters, equally dirty, gathered in a matter of seconds and watched in silence. The ever present mangy, flea-ridden hound kept rubbing his itchy body against our legs as we stood uncomfortably in the developing sadness.

The woman who let us in was not the mother, but a neighbor. She quickly went to the back of the drab little dwelling and brought the crying señora to us. Papa tried to tell

her the case had been hopeless and that everything possible
had been done in an effort to save the child. Her grief was so
deep that he looked at us with a pleading glance. We tried our
best, but in these wretched surroundings no expressions of
sympathy seemed adequate. The fact that the child was men-
tally retarded and would have been even worse had it survived
did not seem important. A life is a life.

All the time we had been talking, the father held the child,
almost as if he feared to put him down. Suddenly, he removed
a stained piece of oilcloth from what served as a dining table,
and placed the baby down upon the table. Humble and
saddened as he was, he asked if we wanted the sheet back. A
linen sheet in these homes is indeed a treasure. We told him no
as we now watched the other children gather around the table
to better examine their dead brother. It gave us an almost eerie
feeling as they examined the burr holes that had been made in
the child's skull.

It was a terrible experience, even when accustomed to
suffering and death. People who have so little, who cannot
feed or clothe themselves, still find the treasure of life precious.
It made us feel our efforts were much more important than
they ever seemed before.

But for every experience with death, there were many more
in which we were responsible for bringing new hope. Vivian
Crosswhite, of Urbana, Illinois, our physical therapist, selected
two young cousins as her source of inspiration. Manuel (aged
three) and cousin Jorge (aged five) had been crippled as a
result of poliomyelitis. Neither could walk alone.

They had never had exercises to strengthen their muscles, or
braces for the support of their legs and feet. Physical therapy
and the science of rehabilitation are unknown in northern
Peru.

Vivian gained their confidence first by placing the boys
together into a warm whirlpool bath. It should have lasted
only half an hour, but they were so surprised and delighted by
the swirling warm water that Vivian did not have the heart to
take them out.

Afterward, she improvised supports made of plaster strips. This help was sufficient to enable Manuel to walk along the length of the physical therapy room floor—about twenty-five feet. He laughed, and his grandmother, who had brought him to the ship, cried. Neither could remember when they had been so happy. Manuel and Jorge were later fitted with splints and eventually braces.

Vivian had already persuaded Chips (the inevitable name for a ship's carpenter) to make exercise bars and a small platform for her department so that such patients could support themselves with their hands and arms while practicing walking. But Jorge, who was older and had been crippled a longer period of time, was fearful and emotional. He even refused to try to stand while supported by his relatives and Vivian. His rehabilitation would later succeed, but was to require considerably more time and patience.

Vivian was both patient and persistent, qualities that were to help enormously in gaining recognition for the need of a rehabilitation center in Trujillo. It had been only a few months since a Congress on Physical Medicine held in Lima had awakened interest in the possibilities for rehabilitation in Trujillo, and some of the more astute saw the added stimulus the presence of the *Hope* would bring.

A branch of the Society of Rehabilitation in Lima was therefore formed in Trujillo. Mrs. Laura Manucci, a compassionate woman and proved friend of HOPE, already was running a special school for deaf and retarded children. She financed this privately, mostly with her own funds and small contributions from others. Señora Manucci agreed to accept the responsibility for heading up the proposed rehabilitation setup.

De Vinatea, the HOPE coordinator, who could hardly keep up with all the new developments growing out of our presence, was elated. He felt that a clinic and training setup could be initiated at Belén, or in the new hospital, if it was ever

completed. He was particularly happy with the many prosthetic devices we had brought with us and promised to make
available to the center. These appliances were primarily donated by veterans of the United States through the People to
People Committee on the Handicapped. Bill McCahill, the
executive director of that committee, had originated this program to make the world aware of the need for rehabilitation,
and we had proved its worth in Asia.

De Vinatea said: "Because the *Hope* has brought many
prosthetic devices which can be furnished free to the local
society, we will be able to accomplish something. These devices are very expensive here in Peru. It would be hard to find
money to buy them at the beginning of a program. But after
we have demonstrated what rehabilitation can do, by means of
the gift of prosthetic devices from HOPE, general interest will
be awakened and there will be private gifts here to support the
work. Then we may well be able to train enough people to
make them so that it would not cost so much to purchase them
here."

Vivian was already training one young woman, Señorita
Edith Barriga Pérez, on the ship and going to clinics in Belén
Hospital three afternoons each week to teach the parents of
crippled children the exercises that they must carry out at
home. Her reputation spread so rapidly that soon she was
treating patients and teaching on the ship all day Tuesday and
Friday and every morning with the exception of Sunday, along
with her heavy schedule at Belén.

The word was getting around that physical therapy could
accomplish great things. Many more people wanted and required the services that Vivian offered, but the Lord Himself
could not have filled the need.

Her comment was, "Good, if we can't take care of them all,
they will really get a training program and rehabilitation
center started here in Trujillo."

In another area, our blood-bank technician, Anita Soto, was having her problems. Not even her native Spanish made it any easier to get blood for the patients or the blood bank from superstitious Peruvians. Some felt that to put their blood into someone else's body was truly the work of the devil. Others thought they would have to spend a week in bed after a donation. At best they would consent to give perhaps one hundred cc's, one-fifth the normal amount. Perhaps unethically, but faced with the necessity of great demand, Anita took advantage of their ignorance of measurement and collected blood in large bottles that always made it appear as if very little had been taken. Some of the potential donors quickly discovered that if they were asked whether they had ever had malaria or syphilis, they should answer affirmatively and their blood would not be taken. Many of them answered "yes" to every question put to them, just to play it safe. Anita finally hit upon the idea of promising each donor a full luncheon meal in exchange for his blood, and immediately her problems became quite different. The Peruvians were so fond of the gringo food that the same donors kept coming back week after week, sometimes day after day, using different names, but unfortunately the same blood. Only a few fooled her, else I fear we would have had many an exsanguinated Trujillian staggering about the streets. Anita was also able to get the blood bank ashore going full blast with the promise of HOPE food, and she trained technicians in the technique of cross-matching and typing. The blood bank at Belén had been transfusing patients for years without cross-matching the blood, and the frequency of serious transfusion reactions was so high that patients feared getting blood almost as much as giving it. Thanks to Anita, those days are now gone in Trujillo.

The importance of the development of an adequate blood bank was dramatically demonstrated by the experience of Dr. Mario Rodríguez, one of our Peruvian surgical residents. So few Peruvians are Rh negative blood types that little attention is paid to blood incompatibilities between mother and unborn child. In our own country this possibility is checked routinely, and when it occurs the patient is watched closely throughout her pregnancy so that anticipated complications can be avoided.

Mario was one of the rarities; he was Rh positive, and his wife was Rh negative. They had already lost two children because of this incompatibility. When Mrs. Rodriguez was delivered at Belén Hospital, her baby became jaundiced almost immediately, a victim of the dreaded erythroblastosis fetalis that had taken her two earlier children. The baby was rushed to the *Hope*, where Anne Watkins, our pediatrician, performed two complete exchange transfusions. In effect, she removed all of the infant's blood, which was slowly killing the child by a "transfusion reaction without a transfusion," and replaced it completely with new blood capable of sustaining life until the youngster could manufacture sufficient normal red blood cells of his own. Anne stayed at this child's bedside for almost forty-eight hours, while Anita kept the fresh blood coming. It was the only child who had ever had a successful exchange transfusion in northern Peru, and the grateful parents christened him Hope. To this day, the streets of Trujillo ring to the call of "Hopito, Hopito," as Mrs. Rodriguez calls for the youngster to come home.

This was a great *regalo* for the staff. Patients were constantly demonstrating their gratitude by bringing gifts, naming their children after nurses or doctors, and it sometimes tore your heart out when you realized how much they were taking from themselves to give to us who already had more than our share. One physician alone was given three chickens, one turkey, twenty-nine baby chicks, two goats, and was offered seven children. Turning down the gift of a child who had been saved from a serious illness became a frequent ritual. The parents felt this life now belonged to us, and they could have it back only if we refused the gift. Some *regalos* were not so easy to reject, even though we knew that to accept a turkey might be taking protein from an entire family for a week or more. Yet the people were very hurt if such offerings were refused. Guinea pigs were another delicacy among the poor of Trujillo, and we were offered so many of these we could have opened our own experimental laboratory. But roasted guinea pig was a fiesta special in many a home. Goats were another *regalo* hard to refuse, but their odor made them even more difficult to accept. When one was invited to the home of a patient or student for dinner, it was not unusual to find the main course goat meat, which unfortunately seemed to retain its same odor, cooked or raw.

We, too, enjoyed giving. Each child that left our hospital took with him his favorite toy from our pediatric ward. Just as we had found in Asia, it was the first real toy many of these children had ever had, and it was their very own. They used to clutch them tightly and just stare at them until they were off the launch, as if they feared the toy might be snatched from them before they reached the safety of the shore.

The plastic identification bands that were placed upon each patient's wrist as they were admitted were not really gifts, but the patients flatly refused to remove them and wore them for ever after. We saw hundreds and hundreds adorning wrists all over Trujillo and Salaverry. Status symbol, or a constant reminder of someone who had been kind to them? Who knows? But, oh, how they treasured them as visible evidence of the *Hope's* presence in Peru!

Not only was the former impression of the "ugly American" changing, but some patients were convinced there was nothing we couldn't do. Dr. Dalton Oliver, an ophthalmologist of Baton Rouge, Louisiana, will never forget his experience. He was standing at the dock with a group of other physicians from the staff, tired from a day's work at Belén and impatiently awaiting the *Rosita* and her guardian Othello to complete the launch run to shore. Suddenly, an old Peruvian Indian carrying a sleeping baby on his back pressed forward through a crowd of curious onlookers.

"I have come for an American miracle," stammered the old man, as he held the figure of the young child out toward the silently watching doctors, and hope mingled with misery and despair on his weatherbeaten face.

The old Indian had walked two hundred miles through the Andes, carrying the listless body of his son, critically ill with an eye tumor. Oliver wasn't certain he could do it, but he was determined to try to save the life of the lad. And he did, though the eye was lost. This belief in our supernatural abilities was summed up by Bill Gallagher, a surgeon from La Crosse, Wisconsin, who said, "They believe we can walk on water."

Oliver later wrote:

Vivid impressions will remain with me the rest of my life. The look on the face of the gnarled old man who came back again and again to shake my hand because our operation had saved him from a life of blindness; the Peruvian Indian who walked two hundred miles over the impossible terrain of the Andes to bring his two-year-old son for an "American Miracle"; little Manuel whose life's dream was to come to the United States and be a houseboy; the faces of schoolchildren tasting cow's milk for the first time; the warmhearted gratitude, from the heads of the country to the lowliest Indian peasant.

And they want to give us presents. Why, we should thank them for giving us back our reason for being alive!

The mayor of Pisac, a small Andean village typical of many to which medical units were sent from S.S. *Hope*.

ABOVE: Peruvian and American medical personnel sing carols to S.S. *Hope's* ward patients on Christmas Day. BELOW: Some of HOPE's staff members before the Christmas tree presented to them by the people of Salaverry.

ABOVE: Hopies receiving certificates from the City of Trujillo at farewell ceremonies that packed the city's stadium. BELOW: A group of barriada youngsters sing "Viva el HOPE" in stadium farewell.

ABOVE: Dr. Fernando Cabieses (left), president of the Peruvian-North American Medical Association, Señora and Mayor Russell de Orbegoso of Trujillo, and Archbishop Pérez Silva of Trujillo at departure ceremonies for the *Hope*. BELOW: Nurse Ann Roden says good-bye to Enrique Vargas, whose respiratory disease was cured after a tracheotomy performed aboard the *Hope*.

ABOVE: Dr. Archie Golden leaves Trujillo stadium ceremonies with Archbishop Pérez Silva; Dr. Golden holds the leather-bound volume of signatures of the city's citizens presented to HOPE by the archbishop. BELOW: Dr. Walsh exchanges farewells with a Peruvian friend at Trujillo stadium. Nurse Helen Ward is at the left.

ABOVE: S.S. *Hope* decked with garlands as it prepares to leave Peru. BELOW: Citizens of Trujillo and the surrounding countryside begin to gather before dawn to pay their respects to the departing ship.

ABOVE: The crowd of well-wishers grows by the hour; the dock at Salaverry. BELOW: Some send flowers, bananas, and other gifts by launch to the Hopies as final gestures of appreciation.

ABOVE: A group of HOPE nurses waves good-bye at the dock. BELOW: The same group gets ready to leave the launch for the S.S. *Hope* for the last time in Peruvian waters. In extreme left foreground is Chief Nurse Dorothy Aeschliman of Sacramento, California, and just behind, to her left, is Nursing Education Director Elizabeth Berry of New Britain, Connecticut.

ABOVE: Some Peruvians crowd in launches for a last farewell to the hospital ship. BELOW: The Hopies have a final good-bye from some 45,000 waving friends on the Salaverry pier.

ABOVE: These shore-bound doctors remained in Trujillo after the S.S. *Hope* left Peru to continue the Project's work by establishing land-based programs in the city's hospitals and medical school. BELOW: Dr. Dorothee Perloff making rounds with a Peruvian doctor and intern in Trujillo's Hospital for Teaching and Training after the S.S. *Hope*'s departure.

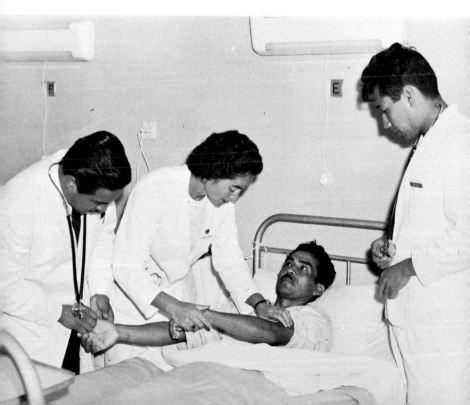

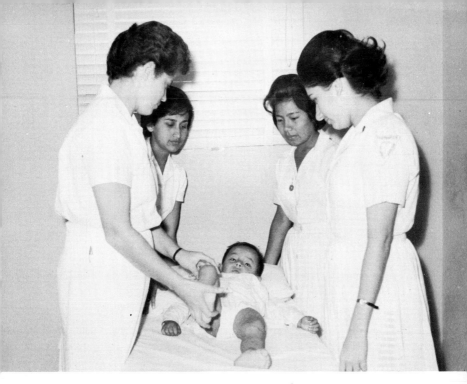

ABOVE: Miss Dorothy Cook instructs physical-therapist trainees in the Hospital for Teaching and Training. BELOW: Mr. Terry Clifford demonstrates X-ray technique in continuing program at the Hospital for Teaching and Training.

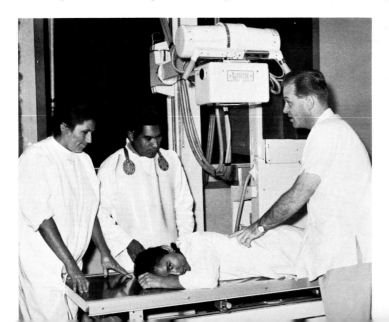

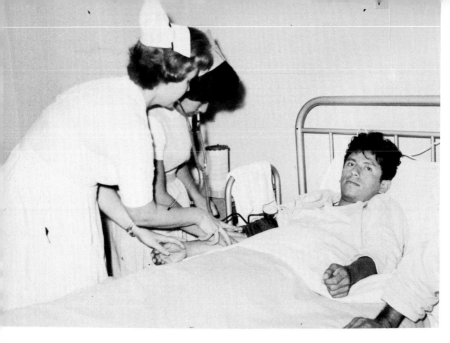

ABOVE: Mrs. Barbara Weaver teaching bedside care on the surgical ward, Hospital for Teaching and Training. BELOW: Nurse Peggy Brenan stays on after the *Hope*'s departure to give instruction in operating-room techniques at the Hospital for Teaching and Training.

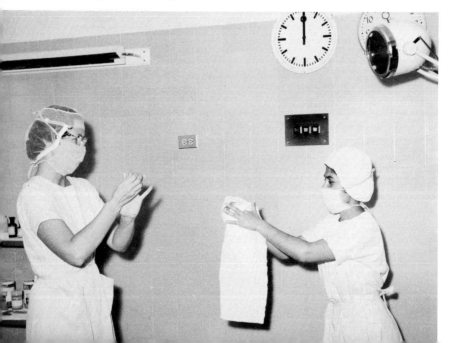

ABOVE: A miniature *Hope*, operated by the Peruvian government, today plies the Amazon; a HOPE public doctor and nurse bring medical education and health to the river settlements long after the parent ship has weighed anchor. BELOW: A typical Peruvian village on the Amazon.

Nurse Betty Carlson of Spokane, Washington, inoculates children in an Amazon settlement in HOPE's continuing program.

ABOVE: An accordionist attracts an audience of Amazon Indians for Nurse Betty Carlson (clapping time), who will give a course in Spanish on personal hygiene. BELOW: Dr. John W. Eiman, a pathologist from Abington, Pennsylvania, with a group of Amazon Indians in Peru.

A young citizen of Peru.

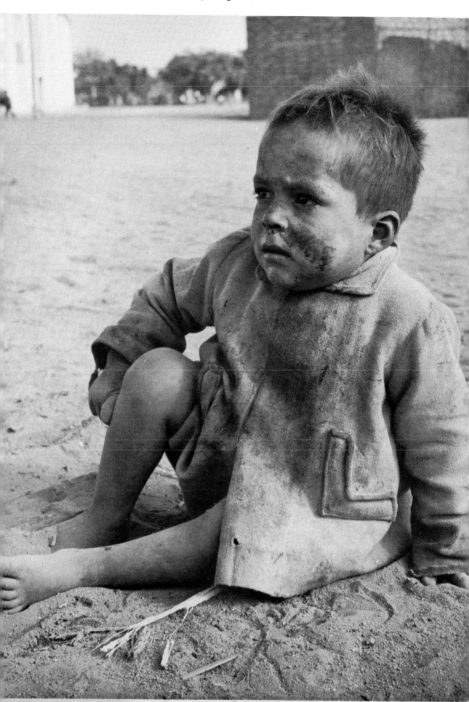

12

The word of our success was now reaching out from Trujillo to Lima and other cities throughout the country; small units of our staff were detached and sent to such places as Talara, Arequipa, Chiclayo, and into the jungle at Iquitos. Requests for help also came in from many other countries of Latin America. This popularity, deserved or not, set off a rumble of discontent among members of the Peruvian Medical Federation, the counterpart of our American Medical Association. This was inevitable, for the physicians, particularly in Lima, were a very proud—even arrogant—lot. Fernando Cabieses, who had accepted the post of Director of the Fondo de Nacional Salud in the new Junta government, did all that he could to help us. The Fondo was similar to the Department of Health, Education, and Welfare in the United States. Cabby himself was accused of every conceivable type of chicanery because of his association with the gringo physicians; and a vocal Castroite minority in the Federation continued to snipe at our activities. The reason behind all this was by now painfully familiar: the physicians feared economic loss if their patients left Lima for treatment in Trujillo.

Many physicians in Lima *were* referring patients to Peruvian colleagues in Trujillo so that they could avail themselves of whatever skills we could offer. We could not stop them from doing so, and felt it none of our concern. These patients in turn still had to be passed on by HOPE's Peruvian admissions committee, and could not even be seen by us in consultation without following procedures set down by the committee at the medical school. Everyone knew about the many summer homes along the beaches that stretched northward up the coast; their wealthy owners could well choose to see their vacation physician instead of their regular man in Lima. The presence of the *Hope* undoubtedly stimulated many to do just this.

If there was any legitimacy at all to the Lima medicos' complaint, this was the basis for it. Yet I could not deny that I felt some undercurrent of delight at this, because for too many years Peru had been dominated by Lima. Prior to 1962, anyone who became seriously ill left his own local physician and quickly went to Lima to find adequate medical treatment. Recognition that a medical center might be growing up more than three hundred miles to the north had many implications that far outweighed the fears of a few greedy men. I could not help but recall how, in the United States, a young surgeon named Mayo started a clinic virtually in a wheat field, only to see an entire city grow around it. No longer did the people of our Midwest have to go to Chicago or Baltimore or Boston for medical care. Wasn't this the same type of sociological change we were encouraging throughout Latin America? Why, then, should we apologize for making Trujillo conscious that it, too, could become a medical center? They had the medical talent; they had a new school; and more importantly they had demonstrated to us that they were quite willing to develop a fresh outlook. Trujillo's doctors were ambitious, too. All this worried some of the old-timers in Lima.

We wanted the Peruvian physicians—and politicians—to recognize that a sick man doesn't care about slogans or promises of economic progress, for he knows he will be unable to participate in this growth. A man blind with treatable or preventable eye disease cannot profit from education or the construction of a new road or industrial plant. A man lame or crippled as a result of a disease he need not have had cannot achieve benefit from land reform or improved agricultural methods. A hungry man has no politics, only a desire to exist. The sick do not have the time or the privilege to be petty.

I can still remember what accepting the referral of a so-called hopeless case from Lima did for both HOPE and Trujillo in the eyes of peoples throughout South America. In the words of the son of the patient, addressed to the medical team who saved his elderly mother:

We traveled all the way from southern Chile seeking medical help for my mother. She suffered from an obstructive jaundice caused by what, because of the symptoms, had been diagnosed as cancer of the pancreas. The doctors in southern Chile had given us little hope, if any, and furthermore were very sincere and honest in saying that it would take a very delicate exploratory operation to determine the actual cause of the obstruction. They did not have the necessary instruments or equipment for this sort of operation. And so, following their advice, we decided to bring her to Lima where my wife and I live.

Again the doctors in Lima offered little hope, but the specialist that examined her was well acquainted with the quality of specialists and surgeons and equipment on the *Hope,* and recommended that we should do everything possible to have her treated on board the ship. We completed an application which he signed and then we went north to Trujillo. We were so fortunate that the day we arrived, and while we were somewhat lost at the Belén clinic, we ran into Dr. Smoller to whom we were able to explain the situation briefly. He referred us to Dr. Gallagher for consultation. After a brief examination he determined the seriousness of her case and the following day she was admitted on board the *Hope* for treatment and surgery.

From that moment on, we can very sincerely say that we have never seen nor experienced such an atmosphere of humanity derived from the treatment offered by the doctors, nurses, and crew of the ship in general as we have witnessed during those twenty-five days that my mother has been on board the ship. It was so contagious that even some patients suffering great pain would make an extra effort to give a smile of thanks to doctors and nurses as they went by their beds.

Yes, the work you are doing is reaching the heart of the people, and of the right people, those who will remember you, your ship and your United States forever for having come to them in time to offer your help to their loved ones. And not only will this be appreciated in Salaverry or in Peru, but by people from other countries in South America, like in our case, and from anyone in the world who knows anything about the humanitarian work you are doing.

In spite of politics and world confusion the "Good Ship Hope" will be remembered. Thanks for having treated my mother and for having determined through very skilled surgery that her illness was *not* cancer. She is leaving the ship today and will be traveling back to Chile as soon as she is completely recovered. She takes back with her good health and gratitude toward you and HOPE. Thanks again.

The signature is not of itself important. The accomplishment of all that HOPE set out to do, manifested in this one instance, was being multiplied many times a week. People were seeking out Trujillo, and they would continue to do so even after the ship left.

Not all our experiences had such pleasant endings. Dr. Anne Watkins was out with a field group in the Amazon jungle across the Andes, where the reputation of HOPE had ranged far and wide by means of the jungle telegraph. They expected only miracles; nothing else would do. Each child she examined was more seriously ill than the one before. One was an infant suffering from a far advanced case of pneumonia, and the village Indians simply watched as Anne did all in her power to save the child. Late that night the youngster died, despite all the gringo magic, and Anne was startled to hear the sound of drums and wailing in the night. She thought certainly her own days were numbered, only to discover that what she heard was a funeral ritual. They were building a simple wooden coffin while they mourned, and brought it to the very hut in which she was supposedly sleeping. She couldn't help weeping as she saw it set quietly in a corner so that she would not be disturbed.

Anne was inconsolable for days, but was this loss really a failure? She was the first specialist ever seen by these people, who, were it not for missionaries, would have no medical care at all, and Anne Watkins and HOPE are still remembered with reverence in that isolated jungle village.

Still another unit in Huancayo, in the mountains inland from Lima, came upon an eight-year-old girl who had been badly burned about a year earlier. The burns, mostly on one side of the body, caused her leg to contract to her abdomen. The arm on the affected side was bound down with scar tissue so that only the wrist could be moved. John Terry, one of our plastic surgeons, wanted her moved to the hospital in La Oroya where she could be prepared for surgery, then transferred to the ship. As always in La Oroya, one delay after another held up the little girl's admission until one morning, almost a month and a half later, the hospital doorman advised Gloria Aguilera that she had a visitor. The visitor was a wrinkled, stooped, gray-haired man dressed in dirty, tattered clothes. He wore sandals cut from automobile tires and bound to his feet with leather thongs. This was the father of the little burned girl, Rosalie, whom we had wanted so much to help. By this time there was only a week remaining before Dr. Terry was to return to his home in Columbus, Ohio, so it was obvious he could not begin the work. The old man had forced a decision by simply bringing Rosalie with him. There was little that the authorities could do other than admit her to the Obrero hospital, pending transfer to the ship.

Rosalie was undersized and emaciated, and there were open wounds, filled with secondary infection, that had to heal before any surgery could be attempted. Virtually mute, she would peer at you with her large dark, wide-set eyes and register no emotion or change of expression, no matter what you did or said to her. Her only response was a conditioned reflex. She cried the moment you lifted her covers to look at the wounds. She feared this meant a change of dressings, and she knew this meant pain almost too great for her to bear, as the dressings always adhered to the exposed sores.

When the bandages had to be changed, therefore, the girls would scrub the only bathtub in the hospital (located in their living quarters) and immerse Rosalie in tepid water, allowing her to soak until the bandages floated free. This helped to reduce the pain and cleansed her wounds at the same time. She was then allowed to sit in a hospital chair in the hall. Before long she became the pet of the whole hospital.

After some two weeks, she began to nod and smile, finally even to talk. When you walked into her room, you were greeted with a shy, winsome grin instead of her former hollow, hopeless stare. Her long black hair had to be cut, for it would get into her open wounds as she moved about the bed. With short hair, and after many baths and some decent food, she now looked neat and happy.

One Sunday Rosalie's family, her mother, father, and little sister, visited us. They stayed for lunch, and not a crumb was left on the table. They hastened to assure us that they had come only to be certain that Rosalie was going to be transferred to the *Hope*, and apologized for having come at lunch hour. We suspect the now articulate Rosalie might have suggested it. Whatever the cause, the meal made everyone happy.

A week later they returned to visit Rosalie once again, for they had heard we were all to be leaving La Oroya soon. The mother, dressed in her best but ragged Indian garb, removed the blanket pouch tied about her shoulders, reached deep in her carryall, and withdrew her hand slowly. Father and little sister watched carefully as mother removed a small package and folded back the wrappings with care. She held up—as if it were pure gold—one very clean egg, and presented it to Gloria. Gloria wept as she took it, for to a family such as this, an egg represented a real sacrifice, a deep and significant sign of gratitude. Gloria always referred to it as "The Golden Egg," and no other experience in Peru, she admitted, better symbolized what we meant to the people there.

Rosalie, though she would require another two years of special rehabilitation work, was already smiling and talking, playing and walking, even before she left the *Hope.*

Others were experiencing the same joy of giving of themselves almost every day. Some five hundred miles away, Helen Ward, our nurse-anesthetist, corrected a cardiac arrest for a local anesthetist in Tarma by demonstrating the technique of external cardiac massage. Dr. Arthur Baptisti, our gynecologist from Indianapolis, brought a patient back to life in the surgical ward at the Belén Hospital by using the same technique, with the addition of mouth-to-mouth resuscitation. In both instances, the patients had been pronounced dead; in neither instance had life really left their bodies. A lifesaving technique that is everyday practice in many areas of the world was a miracle in Tarma and Trujillo. Two lives were saved, and the local staffs were taught how to save more.

One particularly important development was the opening of the first neurology and psychiatry clinic in Trujillo—and in all Peru—under the guidance of Dr. Polo, especially trained by Hope's staff. Before many weeks had passed, people were coming from everywhere in the country, and funds were made available by the Fondo to make the clinic a permanent entity. No more significant step could have occurred in an area with ten times the normal number of convulsive disorders, possibly caused by cases of untreated high fever in childhood. It was such concrete signs of progress that meant ever so much more to us than the "miracles" so attractive to the press.

All our favorable publicity continued to alarm some leaders of the Peruvian Medical Foundation and, of course, the Communists. Stories of bribery and collusion between gringo and local physicians were circulated. Our Peruvian colleagues were undermined by tales that they were unable to work without the help of the Yanquis and were therefore a disgrace to Peru. This was particularly upsetting to the faculty at the medical school, since their appropriation came from the government in Lima, and no amount of assurance from Cabieses could comfort them.

A good reporter rescued us from a most untenable position by bringing the rumors and wild stories into the open. A journalist on one of Lima's leading papers, she learned that one of the leaders of the Peruvian Medical Foundation stopped at a certain café in Lima for a drink each evening. She went to the café, and with little effort engaged him in conversation. It was relatively simple for her to lead him into a discussion of the thing closest to his heart, his dislike of the gringo. He never realized she was a reporter until he read the front page of the morning paper. The fat was in the fire, and when he turned to the editorial page he discovered it was really sizzling.

The editorial blasted the selfishness of the Peruvian Medical Federation, which was mindful only of the economic gain of its members and not the needs of the people. This was, of course, an unfair exaggeration because this Castro-influenced leader did not speak for the great bulk of its membership. But he had represented himself as speaking for all—hence the editorial conclusion. The radio, television, and virtually every paper in the country lambasted the Federation. Chapter after chapter of its membership rejected the opinions of this individual. The faculty in Trujillo issued a statement fully supporting the cooperation between HOPE and the university. People stopped us on the streets to apologize personally. We were flabbergasted at the intensity of the reaction. We knew the Peruvians were emotional, and extremely considerate of the feelings of others, but the nearly universal manifestation of embarrassment was overwhelming. In a matter of a few days the storm subsided, and not too many months later, the leadership of the Peruvian Medical Foundation was changed by an election within its own ranks. The vast majority of physicians, who really do care just as much for human lives as do physicians the world over, had passed judgment. This was to be our last serious crisis in Peru.

13

The months were passing much too fast, and the advantage and disadvantage of being in one location for an entire year becoming clearly apparent. The advantage was to the university, the students, and the people. The disadvantage was that sometimes we could not see the extent of our own progress. Staff members would become discouraged, among them Chief Nurse Dorothy Aeschliman, who was so devoted to Project HOPE that it was difficult for her to tolerate less than perfection. But just seeing a nurse she had trained take over a ward on her own was sufficient to bounce her back from discouragement.

Whenever I returned to the *Hope*, whether from Washington or elsewhere, it was readily apparent to me that a great job was being done. Father Magner, one of our chaplains, drawing on his long cigarette holder and looking for all the world like a redheaded edition of Franklin D. Roosevelt, constantly cautioned: "Don't worry, Boss, don't worry. These are a great bunch of people. They won't let you down, not a single one of them. Just don't push them too hard. They'll know when the time comes how well they have done." He was a great comfort to everyone, walking the decks with the children from the pediatric ward almost every evening, his white cassock billowing in the breeze that accompanied the Peruvian sunset.

There was little to do for recreation, and just as well, for there was little time for it. Some of the staff accumulated their time off and took trips to the fabulous Inca ruins at Machu Picchu, or simply went down to Lima with the intention of going to "Casa Hope" just to sleep. Unfortunately, as soon as the word was out that they were in town, the graciousness of the Limano was such that they were kept on a merry-go-round. They loved it, of course. Bernardo Batievsky, a local business-man who had been educated in the United States, never failed to have groups of them to his home for dinner or to make a car available to them for sightseeing. Fernando Cabieses added to his already overburdened schedule the responsibility for their comfort, and obtained courtesy memberships for them at the Lima Country Club. The change of pace provided by a couple of days of such luxury was probably better than sleep.

One of the staff's favorite spots was the Granja Azul, a restaurant just outside Lima, where for a very modest sum you could eat all the chicken and French-fried potatoes you could hold. The restaurant was built of heavy wood and stone, with large fireplaces inside to take away the chill in the evening air. The chicken was roasted over an open fire, and while waiting you could pass the time drinking a variety of specialties of the house. They were all concoctions of rum or gin, and exotically named "The Passionate Pigeon" or "The Crucial Crucible," or worse.

Others on leave stayed at the historic old Bolívar, where the élite of Peru meet at coffee time. The lobby is classically appointed with dignified tables and furniture, and a large cathedral-like glass dome looms overhead. It is said that if you sit there long enough, you will meet anyone of substance in the entire country, and most certainly any visitor of impor-tance or tourist. I do not recall a single time that I sipped either coffee or a cocktail in the Bolívar that I did not meet someone I knew from somewhere.

It was on these trips to Lima that our staff learned what

time means in another culture. Any visitor to Peru knows of
the difference between Peruvian Time and Gringo Time. If
you were invited to someone's home for dinner, unless American Time was specified, anything up to two hours after the
indicated time was correct. If you arrived at the appointed
time, you would more than likely find your hostess still in
curlers and housecoat and your host in the shower, if at home
at all.

Even knowing this, my good friend Cabby and I had a most
amusing experience with time. We had been invited to the
Presidential Palace for dinner. The time was specific, and
when we discussed it, Cabby said we must be prompt since,
after all, it was a presidential invitation. We arrived promptly
at 8:00 P.M. to find ourselves completely alone with an attentive
servant and a more than ample supply of alcohol. By nine
thirty other guests began arriving, and within another hour the
last of them came on the scene. According to protocol, not
until then did the President join the party. He required a
drink, and there were the usual toasts, so after a three-and-one-
half-hour cocktail period we finally went in to dinner.

We also learned that if you were invited from five to seven,
this meant coffee or tea and cake. Eight o'clock meant cock-
tails, and almost any hour after that meant dinner. Our permanent staff deserved every invitation they received, whatever
the hour, and we encouraged them to accept them as the best
way to learn to know and understand the people. Our nurses,
technicians, and secretaries in particular did yeoman service
both on and off the ship. Even on occasions when they cried
out for sleep, they would attend some necessary social function, and contrive to look as fresh as newly painted pictures.

Adaptability was the key to fitting into the social world of
Casa Grande or Cartavio, the W. L. Grace hacienda, with the
same ease as in a mestizo's home in the barriada or a trainee's
home in Salaverry. The Peruanos made it easy for them, for

everywhere the staff went they were welcomed with the same affection.

They had the added chore of welcoming each group of new rotators while seeing off each old group with sadness. With December came a new, eager group of rotators, bringing news from home and, of course, thoughts of Christmas even though the summer weather in Trujillo did little to add to the Yuletide spirit. But as Ken Seagrave, a radiologist from Buffalo, recalled for me, there were subtle notices on the bulletin board that Christmas cards for the States should be mailed early and that the ship carried the official HOPE Christmas card. Unfortunately, it was not too imaginative that year, but Flash Gordo, the intrepid, mammoth-sized local photographer, was well aware of the American Christmas greeting habit and stepped into the breach. Never one to miss a fast *sole,* he came on board with an ample supply of cards of his own design, overpriced but local. It was nothing more than a black-and-white postcard photo of the good ship *Hope* in Salaverry, under which was inscribed *Feliz Navidad y Prospero Año Nuevo.* The positive salesmanship of the "Flash" was irresistible, and as Ken said, "Fat Stuff's *prospero* was assured."

Sometime during the month, the alert chairman of the ship's recreation committee decided that there should be a contest to make everyone very aware of the Christmas season. A very special, devilishly hot bottle of *pisco* rum would be given to the residents of whichever cabin came up with the most original and unusual door decoration. For those with imagination and even a minimum of artistic ability, this was a real challenge. In less than a week's time the previously colorless passageways were transformed into spectacular Christmas galleries.

The scenes varied from the classic religious portrayals to Christmas on Machu Picchu. One somewhat irreligious or very homesick soul even made a Playboy pinup "angel" as his central theme. There was a stained-glass church window of colored cellophane. One door displayed a simple manger constructed from wooden tongue depressors, with a cotton lamb at its foot. Still another arranged colorful, cutout prints of ancient *huacos* (the old Peruvian drinking vessels) around four miniature Christmas trees. One, entitled "Christmas Eve, Salaverry, Peru," showed a jolly Santa in his sleigh riding through the skies over the good ship *Hope* as she lay at anchor, with seven pink llamas pulling the sleigh.

The Hopies did not keep the Christmas spirit to themselves. Some ten days before the 25th a notice was circulated among the staff suggesting a HOPE-sponsored Christmas Party for the children of Salaverry. Contributions were taken up both from the staff and ship's crew. In no time at all, a substantial amount was collected, and shopping trips to Trujillo for toys and candy became a daily ritual. Hundreds of toys were purchased, and I daresay the shoppers added a little more to the kitty each time it was their turn in town.

The party was to be held in the very center of Salaverry, on the Saturday before Christmas. The district councilman offered the use of his headquarters, and although the party was scheduled to begin at ten in the morning, several hundred excited children were on hand before nine. Ted Wormke, our first mate, who happily did resemble St. Nick in girth and laugh, was appropriately dressed for the occasion. Loudspeakers filled the town with traditional Christmas music. Like youngsters anywhere, the children kept trying to peek into the windows, hoping to catch an advance glimpse of the treasures in Santa's sack, or indeed of our sweating Santa himself.

Although "dress-up" clothes were uncommon in Salaverry, many of the children had been very specially groomed and scrubbed for the occasion. They were of all ages, those too tiny to walk being dutifully carried by an older brother or sister.

As the hour approached, the children were given instructions, and without any fuss lined themselves up in two long columns at right angles to the door of Santa's shop.

Promptly at ten, amid shouts of "Merry Christmas!" the festivities began. No one there will ever forget the happy faces of those youngsters as they came away clutching rubber balls, checkerboards, dolls, toy trucks, and airplanes. Some tore the wrappings off immediately so that they could inspect their new possessions; others just held them in disbelief, the first toy they had ever owned. Each child was given a bag of candies and a container of milk to go along with his gift. Soon all of the Hopies were surrounded by groups of youngsters happily playing with their new toys, some singing, others dancing in the street. Knowing of the American fondness for the traditional Christmas tree, these poor people of Salaverry had somehow found one—where the Lord only knows. The most anemic but gorgeous fir tree in the world was presented to the *Hope* for its Christmas on board. Our Yuletide was now complete.

Christmas Eve was quiet; most of the staff was in a reflective mood, and homesick in a way that only those who have been away on this night themselves can fully understand. They sang a few carols, put some last-minute decorations on the tree, and attended the religious service of their faith.

The following morning the entire HOPE family gathered informally in the lounge to celebrate. Each of us had one gift provided by another staffer who drew the recipient's name by lot. The lounge was decorated from a treasure chest of Christmas remembrances placed on board by the parents of some of our nurses before we left home. There was even a small artificial tree, covered with tinsel and lights. When all were assembled, the chief of staff read aloud a letter from Eldon Ellis, a surgeon who had returned home with the previous rotation yet who had taken the time to write at some length, perhaps remembering the special poignance of holidays spent away from home. He wrote in part:

For all of you in Peru on the Great White Ship . . . I would like to remind you that, as you spend this Christmas away from your own homeland, you are the greatest demonstration of the angel-announced message of the Christ-Child: "Peace on Earth! Good Will Toward Men!" . . . You may be assured that with the dawn of the Christmas morn, I would like no greater gift than to be with you. Short of that, I send my deepest love, and admiration for a "Family" which I shall cherish for so long as I live. God Bless You!

Accompanying his letter was a parody Ellis had written on "The Night Before Christmas," especially for the Hopies in Salaverry, and which was also read to much appreciative laughter.

Afterward we wandered to the flight deck and admired our scraggly, eighteen-foot fir tree, standing unadorned yet so noble and meaningful, the gift of the people of Salaverry, which must have been brought many miles from the Sierra to this coastal desert beach. It symbolized the true meaning of Christmas between peoples who only months before had mistrusted each other. Today, Christmas Day in 1962, it meant "Yanqui, stay with us."

[14]

The days following Christmas were busy and exciting. The affection of the people was everywhere made evident, even by the town eccentric, an elderly lady who collected a small tribute from each automobile as it paused at a stop sign just before entering the main town square. Everyone good-naturedly paid her the "tax" she charged, and no one doubted that it served to feed an entire family. Suddenly she effected a policy change for the gringos only. Each time one of our vehicles came by, her hand would quickly be withdrawn as she excitedly said, "No, no, not from you! You have already done too much to help my people!" With that would come a toothy grin and a wave, indicating we were free to pass. Cabdrivers lowered their rates for us, and in many instances would not accept any fare at all.

Our teaching program was now in full swing. Dr. Acuña himself asked Dr. Al Hurwitz to prepare a set of bylaws for Belén Hospital. It was to be the first set of bylaws for the operation of the hospital since Belén had been built. The Belén staff had already begun to have their first general staff meetings, death conferences, and record-room meetings. The staff itself developed a new pride and dignity, and were more willing to pass on their knowledge to the students. Members of the student federation, who had at first been the most hostile, now were our strongest friends, and came to us with a plea to

leave teachers behind after the ship left. They told us that we
had created an entirely new atmosphere and relationship
between their own faculty and themselves. Along with the
increased amount of personal teaching they received, a social
change was taking place.

Herb Bloom, our oral surgeon, began a concentrated course
in oral surgery for the dentists of northern Peru. They came to
Trujillo from miles around, and attended his lectures three
evenings a week. Not a single absentee was recorded through
the almost two full months of the course. Hardly an evening
passed that some of our nurses or technicians were not invited
to the homes of their students or patients. The village of
Moche, halfway between Trujillo and Salaverry, previously
only a collection of houses on the side of the road, now became
a center of nightly entertainment and hospitality. Peggy Brenan, one of our nurses, took part in a *marinera* dancing contest
with one of her students from Moche, and reached the semi-
finals.

Patients nearly overran the hospital and clinics as the people
became aware that the time for the *Hope's* departure was not
far off. We had another mission to begin, in the neighboring
country of Ecuador, and the word had spread that we could
not be persuaded to remain longer than originally scheduled.
Belén Hospital was also more crowded than ever, and the
surgeons, who at one time had seemed both anti-Lister and
anti-Pasteur, were working efficiently and cleanly. Trujillo had
come alive as a medical center, and the faculty and students
could both feel it. They looked longingly at the new hospital
for teaching and training on which construction had ceased
some months before, and prayed for a miracle to get it moving
again. This miracle finally came into being through the combined efforts of Fernando Cabieses, the Fondo de Nacional
Salud, and the Ministry of Health of the Peruvian government.
At Cabby's urging, funds were made available for the comple-

tion of the hospital and the purchase of its equipment, but there was a condition. That condition was that Project HOPE would provide consultant, administrative, medical, and nursing teaching staffs to the university for a three-year period following the departure of the ship from Salaverry.

The tribute to us in this condition was breathtaking. Here, resisted and possibly even despised by some only months before, a three-million-dollar installation was to be completed only if we should agree to remain. The faculty at the medical school, with the full support of the students, threw their weight behind the government's request. Dean Olguin, Jorge de Vinatea, and our old antagonist Alfredo Acuña pledged fullest cooperation. The new hospital was to be affiliated with the medical school, and would be called the Hospital for Teaching and Training as evidence of their desire to continue the giant steps already taken in advancing medical and nursing education. Living quarters would be provided for our staff, who would continue to be represented on the University Council by whomever we designated as chief.

It was simply too good to be true. Everything we had believed in, everything we had fought for, everything we had promised the doubters at home was coming to fruition. The seed of unrest we had planted in our Peruvian colleagues had borne a flower of progress that would bloom for years to come. The writers of anti-Yankee slogans would now have before them a House of Mercy completed because the Yankee had come to help them. It would mean more work and more staff. We were still supporting staff in Indonesia and providing the training skills for our rehabilitation center in Vietnam. Now we were asked to take on an even larger task, but it was one we could not refuse. We in turn had a condition we wished to make a part of our bargain: the initiation of a medical program in the Amazon River basin area in Iquitos and extending southward toward Pucalpa.

It was our hope that we could institute a health education program in this broad expanse of land which, though covering one third of Peru, nonetheless remained relatively unpopulated and equally unproductive. The reason: disease. The life span in this area was below twenty-six years, less than the average in countries like India and Pakistan. It had long been the dream of a young architect, now Peruvian President Belaunde Terry, that the future of Peru would be determined by the development of the Amazon region. Cabby had talked with me about it, and we both concluded that its economic development depended upon improved health. Populated primarily by Indians with minimal education and maximal reliance upon superstition, any such undertaking in this area would be a tremendous task. We asked only for a chance to begin, and the authority to coordinate the program through the University of Trujillo.

Before agreeing to this condition, the government suggested that we take a quick trip to the region so that we would know for what we were asking. Shortly thereafter Cabby, Archie Golden, Ed Movius (a cameraman who had been with HOPE in Salaverry and who would record some of what we saw) and I took off in an old but reliable DC 4, bound for the jungle interior. The flight took us first over the barren coastal desert, then, after only sixty miles, into the foothills of the Andes, and over their snow-covered crests. As we began our gradual descent, the snow suddenly dissolved into the lush tropical green of the rain forest. For miles over the horizon, as far as the eye could see, there was a mass of trees so close together that no space was discernible between them. This panorama was broken only by an occasional muddy tributary of the Amazon. Wherever there was water, there was a cluster of thatched roofs and people working in the small clearings.

The closer we approached the ground, the hotter the plane became. The humidity of the jungle seemed to reach even thousands of feet into the air. Cabby and I became more excited every moment, for in viewing the river-studded landscape from above, it was obvious that the best plan for developing the Amazon Valley in the near future depended wholly upon water-borne transportation—on shallow-draft hospital ships and schools. There were no air strips hacked out of the jungle, for the overgrowth was so rapid that it was hardly worth keeping them clear unless they were to be used daily. We could not help thinking what a failure in one of the plane's engines would mean. It would take literally weeks for anyone to reach us.

Suddenly, in the midst of the green lay the wide expanse of the mouth of the Peruvian part of the Amazon River, bordered on one side by the jungle city of Iquitos and on the other by the inevitable cluster of temporary wooden houses—the barrio sister city.

Iquitos is the capital city of the department of Loreto, and the naval base for the "inland branch" of the Peruvian Navy. The city itself we found beautiful, with most of its buildings constructed of white or pink plaster walls. It was colorful, busy, and friendly. A great deal of shipping came in through the length of the river from Brazil, giving the town a seaport flavor. The naval authorities had been designated as our hosts for the visit, since they were more aware of local problems than anyone other than the health officer.

The naval base was a paradise by comparison with the surrounding jungle. Built on a small hill, across a bend in the river from the city, its buildings were modern and air conditioned. There were the officers' club, swimming pool, and school for the children of base personnel. Most of the naval officers here had either been trained at Annapolis or had received graduate education in the United States, and their base resembled many that I have seen at home.

We were billeted in quarters set aside for visiting officers, took a cold shower, and were off on our survey. Here, as everywhere in Peru, no false effort was made to hide the bad and stress the good. The public health officer took us to the Iquitos Hospital, where several hundred people occupied only two hundred beds. The pediatrics ward was filled to overflowing, with many cases of kwashiorkor (protein-deficiency starvation) lying unattended. The small bodies of the children were bloated like fattened toads, and two were in the terminal stage of the illness. There was neither proper food nor appropriate medication to give them. Much of the hospital was without electricity, and the overworked staff appeared to be almost as ill as some of the patients. There were no nurses or technicians to be seen. The meager staff, together with the physicians assigned by the Ministry of Health, were responsible for the care of hundreds of thousands of people in the entire area. How could they possibly administer, educate, and do technicians' work as well? Health education at the lowest level was going to be a must, for in the long run only preventive medicine would save lives or lengthen their span.

We then visited some of the small settlements, and found families of twelve and fourteen living in wooden huts some three feet above the ground, resting on wooden supports. This was to keep the snakes out, for snakebite is a common cause of death, particularly among the children. We later were shown a member of the boa constrictor family some eighteen feet long and almost as many inches across. It had been captured for sale to a zoo, and we wondered how the thatched roofs with no sides to the hut would keep a hungry crawler like that one out. Through interpreters we discovered that it had taken four men to capture the snake, which they thought would be very docile, having recently consumed a small pig. This snake kills by crushing his victim, and even when sluggish, after his meal, the lengthy reptile had succeeded in breaking one Indian's arm during the struggle. Now, though in his primitive cage, he scared me almost to death. I began to wonder why worldwide teaching and training should have become my personal mission.

The people lived simply, and viewed us with obvious skepticism. Only after they had been assured that we were physicians who were trying to develop some means of helping them, and not just picture-snapping tourists, their reserve softened somewhat. The women were dressed only in cloth skirts; most of the children wore no clothes at all. Skin eczemas of every kind abounded. Teeth were a rarity. When present at all, they were decayed. Plentiful vegetation was all around, but ignorance of what should be eaten precluded good nutrition. The river was filled with fish, and scrawny chickens ran loose everywhere. We never did figure out how anyone knew whose chicken was whose, but every once in a while an agile youngster would catch a couple and take them into his hut, obviously for the day's main meal.

We traveled up the Amazon on navy gunboats, which are flat-bottomed and exact sister ships of the famous old China gunboat, the U.S.S. *Panay*, sunk by the Japanese on the Yangtze River in 1937. These boats went on monthly patrols along various parts of the swiftly flowing river, which has a current, we were told, over nine knots. These craft keep in touch with the scattered population throughout the area. They drew less than four feet of water—some said two—and were able to leave the river and move up the shallow, muddy tributaries we had seen from the air. The Amazon itself is wide and deep, but in the dry season drops more than nine feet in depth, and some of the streams that empty into her dry up completely. We were somewhat puzzled as to the mission of the gunboats, other than to show the flag. We soon determined that a firm recommendation should be made to convert these into little *Hopes*. This dream has become an actuality, and some navy ships have been fitted out with operating rooms and staffed with doctor, nurse, dentist, and teacher.

We returned to Iquitos before dark and spent most of the

evening at our quarters. The naval officers were most kind, and entertained us royally at their isolated base. They were so hospitable they even tried to provide us with female companionship to "enable us to relax more fully," and it took the most tactful yet vigorous protestation to dissuade them from this courtesy.

The next day we journeyed upriver to see if we could find some areas where pilot programs could be carried out. We traveled this time in two small motorboats, driven with the same gay abandon with which the Peruano drives his automobile. It was the rainy season, and water descended in torrents. Debris from the jungle, including logs twice the length of the boats, were floating free in the water, and how we ever missed some of them I shall never know. Had we struck one, the wooden bottom of our craft might easily have been staved in, and the deadly piranhas have swarmed about for a meal.

As we proceeded upriver, we noticed that wherever there was a missionary settlement, the land was cleared and the jungle pushed back. Healthy-looking cattle were munching the grass, and a variety of crops were growing. On either side of these areas, villages of Indians lived beneath the trees, foraging for their food. An occasional chicken or lean cow could be seen. Each new sight made us more determined than ever to see that a program was begun on the river. This land could be made productive, its people healthy. Belaunde's dream was not visionary, but a practical plan that had a chance if it began with health first and roads and factories later.

After some two hours we turned off into a tributary, which opened into a gorgeous lagoon. It was almost a movie setting, and despite the rain we could see a large settlement on the hill above. The boats glided to the shore, and Cabby and I jumped out, prepared to rush up the hill to meet the village welcoming committee. After three steps up the muddy side of the bank, we found ourselves flat on our faces, covered with mud from head to foot. This was hardly the way to make an impression, yet it seems we could not have done better. Every man, woman, and child in that village turned out to laugh, gesturing, dancing, and slapping their naked hips in delight.

The comic relief over, we made our study. The children presented a false picture of health, their bellies fat from protein deficiency and too much carbohydrate. When we inspected the food being prepared, the reason was obvious. Yucca, a sort of sweet potato, is the daily staple, and seems to grow everywhere; it is filling and stops gnawing hunger, but as an exclusive diet it produces a condition verging on beriberi. The corners of the villagers' mouths were cracked open, their tongues red and smooth. Rickets was common. Almost all were barefoot, and hookworm was rampant.

Monkeys were the only source of meat, and they were not too common. The villagers killed the monkeys by using a blow gun and a dart tipped with curare. The hunters demonstrated their fantastic accuracy to us, but I found it hard to believe that their best efforts could bring in enough monkeys to feed the whole village. They insisted that we try the tough and grainy monkey meat, which even Escoffier could not have made tasty.

In a corner of one of the huts, several women sat chewing maize. After amply working it over, they spat it into large wooden bowls. This was the first stage in making *chincha*, the Amazon version of corn liquor. We were to be given the privilege of sampling this, too, before the day was over, and had we not seen it being made, we might have enjoyed it. The prime source of income for the village was ropemaking, and we saw the thin lines of hemp hung out on a line, waiting to be braided.

We learned, however, that despite the primitive appearance of the village and the obvious ignorance that abounded, there was an intense desire to learn. Here, just as in every village along the river, the naked little girls had a dress tucked away that they would put on to go to school, a three-hour trip each way by canoe, so that they could learn to read and write. We concluded that health education should be incorporated in the grade-school curriculum, for any children who wanted to study this much would most certainly learn. Medical treatment and immunization for the elders would have to be sandwiched in when possible so as to keep their support, but our plan on the Amazon was to be built upon reaching those children who at least survived to school age. Only one out of four were currently making it past the age of three in this area, an appalling price to pay for ignorance in the twentieth century.

Each day thereafter was like the day before. Malaria was everywhere, and the population worn and weary. We became fired with the ambition to get something started, and were anxious to return to Trujillo. The authorities wanted to be certain we took time to see everything we wished, and it was only after three of us were down with immobilizing dysentery that we were able to persuade them we had seen enough. Then back we went to Trujillo, exhausted, dehydrated, and determined. The Amazon was a challenge, and we wanted to play a part in surmounting it. The health authorities in Lima concurred, and we agreed to stay in Trujillo to help them organize the Hospital for Teaching and Training.

[15]

Back in Trujillo, we found that word had leaked out that we were going to leave a staff behind after the ship pulled up anchor for the United States. The people were overjoyed and, except for an occasional physician, the medical community was enthusiastic. Even in Lima, *La Prensa*, the country's leading newspaper, published by former Foreign Minister Pedro G. Beltrán, came out with a warm editorial. Marcella de Ganoza, our loyal volunteer and dear friend in Trujillo, sent me the following letter and her own translation of the editorial. It was so sincere and charming, even with its lapses in English, that I am certain she will not mind my reproducing it here. Her translation so reflects the genuine warmth of her people toward HOPE that her own words cannot be improved upon:

Trujillo, 17 de Enen de 1963

DEAR DR. WALSH:

It is a pleasure for me to write you sending you this article that appears in: *La Prensa*, 14 of January 1963, which I hope you will like it. I make a translation the best I could. I think it took me a hundred hours.

The writer is a girl more less of my age. She went once to the ship and I show her around it. She asked me all the information, I gave it to her the best I could, but I told her that what was more interesting was the sentimental part of the project, and how it has been received by our people. This is why I specially enjoyed reading it.

My life will be very sad when the *Hope* leaves, and I decided I won't think about it. This will be a great loss for all Peruvians, but we have received all their benefits, and I understand that we have to share.

My best memories for you. I hope will see you very soon.

MARCELLA DE GANOZA

THE "GRINGOS" WON'T LEAVE US

Maybe in a future time the rivers of our jungle will see anchored a white ship, the "hope junior," a small hope. Even though another big ship that has done miracles in the coast of Salaverry will be leaving the first of March to their port of origen, the organization "People to People" will leave their generosity well anchored in Peru. And from another "Ship" an exchange of doctors, knologies, and good-will continue, in the Medical School of Trujillo, for an indifinet time because when the "Gringos" give, they give with full hands.

In Trujillo a new word has entered the vocabulary of the people. Maybe before this word was used despreciativelly, or with rencor, with that hate which politicans without scrupulous usually put in the mouths of the innocents. "Gringo" is no longer synonim of yanky capitalism, of injust, of economical monopoly "Gringo" since May of 1962, constitutes for the Peruvians he who saves lifes and consoles their pains. He who smiles, protects while giving his time without any gain, his youth, and his experience and all which he brought in his luggage "Gringo" is their board of salvation, of flesh and blood.

And so the *Hope* leaves us, with complete satisfaction of having done its duty. The most fruitiferous Embassy, better than any other diplomat mission of the world, because it does good to simple people and changes in their souls their hostility to confedence. Floating proffesorship where each operation and each gesture was done in a team, to specialize Peruvian doctors in the most economical University in History. Perfect Hospital, where the marvelles of its instrumental and equiptment, with the plethoric human feeling of compassion, of comprehensive acts.

To someone who has never been in line a hospital for the

poor, or someone who has never seen this line, does not know what it is to support the hours and the heat in a sick body so many times with the anguish of the children left at home without any one to care for them. So many other, who have spent their last savings in a passage ticket, arrive at noon when the doctors leave and have to return again, to exhaust oneself once more.

That crowd that is always wayting and exercising their patience, is no more afraid of the neighbor that is dirty and carries his sickness in his face. Those people know now to suffer in silence, even the cries that so may times crown the monnotonous rutune of their hospital days; the bad temper gestures of nurses and doctors.

That same crowd was making the line in the Hospital Belén of Trujillo. But the goal, the door of the medical office that approached slowly, had another look, the crowd had the smile of a hope.

Shaved heads, with bow-ties, faces burned by the sun, and airs of athletics childrens, such were the *Hope* doctors. In their immense hands they had magic powers and the people sucumbed to their affection capable of giving toys in Salaverry for Chitsmas, in Trujillo, in Peru and in the whole world.

Such is the memory that they will soon leave. So they won't go, soon others "Gringos" will come, with the same expressions. And an entire country will know that another country is a generous friend to them.

Two important visitors came at this time to visit the *Hope*. One, Dr. Raymond White, Director of the Division of Environmental Medicine of the American Medical Association, had been requested by the Board of Trustees of the Association to visit the Project and bring back his evaluation. The AMA had supported us financially and actively since our inception, and decided they would now make an onsite inspection. We were delighted, and Dr. White and his wife, who had been a registered nurse, spent a week with us. They had the opportunity to see every facet of our work, talk to our staff, and examine our failures as well as our successes. Ray, before he left, told our staff that he was overwhelmed by what he had seen. His only problem, he added, was "how to reduce what I have seen and felt to words so that I can make a proper report to the American Medical Association."

Our second January visitor was Ambassador Douglas Henderson, who was then the American Chargé d'Affaires at our Embassy in Lima. Doug had been through the difficult period after the rupture of relations between our two countries following the "revolution." Now that official recognition had been given, he was acting until the arrival of the newly appointed ambassador. He himself was shortly afterward named Ambassador to Bolivia, and I cannot help but feel it was in part the result of his exemplary performance in Peru during those troubled months.

Ambassador Henderson spent several days with us, but during his visit lived at the Turista Hotel in the center of town, which in his honor flew the American flag until he departed. He told me that it was the first time in recent memory that the American flag had been flown in Trujillo without precipitating a serious incident, and he attributed this demonstration of friendship for the United States directly to Project HOPE.

To us, most exciting of all, however, were the developments in the Barriada Esperanza, developments that could almost be called a social revolution. The barriada residents were already overflowing with pride in their accomplishment at having developed the most successful outpatient clinic in the area. LaVerne kept warning them that the ship would soon be leaving and that she and her successor, Pauline Dickey, would be unable to leave them with a limitless supply of free medication, clean water, and the other essentials for the continuation of the clinic. Guidance they could give in abundance, and we felt certain Peruvian physicians would take over the medical responsibilities without compensation. But the inhabitants of the barriada had now become accustomed to adequate medical attention, and Señor Burgos and his council were asked to face facts. Archie Golden, our pediatrician, who had agreed to remain in Trujillo as our staff leader and coordinator following the departure of the *Hope,* was as worried as the girls. But they had come up with an idea and had only to sell it to the Barriada Council. It all hinged upon water.

The people of the barriadas either took their water from a polluted stream, bought it from a man who sold it by the can, or cajoled and threatened the city government until they were provided with drinking water. Archie felt that if they would only drill for water, they could not only supply it to all the inhabitants of Esperanza, but could sell it to the other, less progressive, barrios and obtain funds to support their clinic from the profits. Finally the decision was made to dig a well.

Pauline Dickey was placed in charge of the operation, a singularly strange responsibility for a public health nurse. A location was selected, and to the amazement of all, rich and poor alike, the digging was begun. Excavating by handshovel in the coastal sands is not easy, and at every step the sides of the hole had to be shored up, else it would fill with sand as fast as it was emptied. After the hole had reached some fifteen feet in depth, with no water in sight, discouragement set in. Just when all seemed lost, the people at Casa Grande, so impressed with the evidence of self-help in Esperanza, sent down a drilling rig and crew, and the work continued. They struck water at seventy feet, and were so elated you would have thought it was oil. Now the problem of a pump arose. The W. R. Grace Company, through its hacienda at Cartavio, donated a pump, and the townspeople were in business.

But now that they had tasted success, they wanted more. The well must be protected by a strong well house, but there were no funds for the necessary bricks and plaster. A committee was appointed; and suddenly one morning, from some mysterious source, a pile of bricks large enough to construct six well houses appeared at the side of the well. No one dared ask the committee from whence they came, and no one reported any missing. An architect donated his services, and the well house was completed, soon to be enhanced with supplementary pipelines to remote corners of the barriada.

Construction of a new Posta Médica was to have begun next, but somewhere along the line the building was converted into a jail. Nevertheless, the medical clinics were improved. The effort instigated by LaVerne Fakkema only a few months before had stimulated medical care and public health and dug a well. Most significant, it had awakened an entire community. Esperanza had indeed become a *genuine* community, not just another barriada.

On board ship, the wards continued to fill with the sick, the maimed, and the needy. Pathos, tragedy, and success were intermingled. Pris Strong and Helen Ward were thrilled with the progress of their anesthesia trainees, and felt that one in particular was almost capable of beginning a course for the training of others. Unfortunately, the prejudice of the American-trained Peruvian physicians against nurse-anesthetists equaled that of some of our own unreasonable men at home, even though it would have been far safer to use a highly competent nurse-anesthetist in preference to a poorly trained physician. The girls could only hope that Archie Golden could prevail against his Peruvian colleagues after the departure of the ship.

Barbara Schwenk, our senior laboratory technician from Minneapolis, was so pleased with her students that she had already determined to remain in Peru with Dr. Golden and the others. She had heard our report on the Amazon and was anxious to go to the hospital at Iquitos and attempt to institute a laboratory training program for technicians in Loreto. Margaret Brenan from Tiona, Pennsylvania, was another who had decided to stay until she was satisfied that Dr. Acuña would accept the authority of a strong operating-room nursing staff. Peggy, as we all knew her, had made many friends among the people of Trujillo, and she could not bring herself to leave her job unfinished.

It was the spirit of Archie, Barbara, Peggy, and so many others that overcame all suspicion and prejudice, that really reached the people of Trujillo. Even at Belén Hospital, where our acceptance had been in doubt, there was concern that we would confine our efforts only to the new Hospital for Teaching and Training after the ship left, and they did everything possible to make us know we would be welcome at Belén as well. We of course intended to work in both hospitals to avoid a situation that would have split the medical profession in this now exciting community right down the middle.

As a matter of fact, Belén Hospital had already benefited handsomely from our training. Gloria Hammond, our electrocardiographic technician from Palo Alto, had trained three capable technicians. This enabled Dr. Bocanegra, the chief of internal medicine, and Dr. Bendezu, an excellent cardiologist, to improve immeasurably what was already the strongest department at both Belén and the medical school. The laboratory at Belén Hospital had arranged for the employment of seventeen HOPE-trained technologists, and were promised a supervisor for another year.

Another satisfying event of the winter was the establishment of medical libraries at both Belén Hospital and the medical school. More than nine thousand miscellaneous medical texts were catalogued and distributed. In addition, similar sets of three hundred basic texts were given to the medical schools at Arequipa and to San Marcos in Lima. The lack of textbooks in Peru was appalling, and a good medical text cost between eighty and one hundred American dollars. Such a prohibitive price made private purchase virtually impossible. Most grateful of all were the students. It had been necessary for them to study in shifts, each taking a turn on a different book. Each student who satisfactorily completed his assignment on board the *Hope* received appropriate recognition in the form of a certificate and a more tangible remembrance of the experience: a "graduation present" of a set of twenty textbooks, courtesy of the book publishers of the United States and the Good Ship *Hope*.

[16]

So it went day after day, everyone frantically trying to finish what they had come to do. The Trujillanos who had become so close to us spent more and more hours with our staff. The archbishop became an almost daily visitor, and worked feverishly to keep the local HOPE committee intact so that the follow-up program would not fall by the wayside. The final group of rotators, who arrived in early February, 1963, were absorbed into the community life as if they were returning home, instead of entering a strange environment. Cultural shock was a thing of the past.

Shortly before our departure from Peru, the celebrations began in earnest. Among the first of these was the performance of a long "tone poem" in which the children of Barriada Esperanza thanked the Hopies for their "angelic love"—*Miss Fakkema en especial.* One late February afternoon, a spontaneous celebration took place in the local football stadium. It was the best-kept secret of the year, for it was not until about two days before, that the HOPE staff even heard rumors of it. More than twenty thousand Trujillanos turned out to pay their respects. Among the acts were dance demonstrations and a team of performing horses and every other conceivable form of entertainment. Patients, or families of patients who had been treated on board, made up most of the crowd, and they brought flowers and gifts of all kinds for the doctors and nurses. Our staff was seated on a platform in the middle of the stadium, and it was a toss-up who cried the most, we in our embarrassed gratitude at this show of affection, or they with their sincere feeling of regret that we would soon be leaving. The climax of the occasion was a performance by the barriada children, who repeated their song and then suddenly turned around and flipped large cards on their backs that spelled out Viva El Hope.

In a more somber tone, the Archbishop, His Excellency Pérez Silva, spoke on behalf of the entire community, and his words were so beautiful and told so much of what Hope had truly accomplished that we must share them in part with you:

During nine months, from the 26th of May of last year, the white silhouette of the *Hope* has given the peaceful harbor of Salaverry all the enchantment of an oasis in the midst of the desert. To it have come thousands of sick from Trujillo, from the neighboring provinces and even from the most distant corners of the country. All these sick were attended with exemplary devotion and skill, and even more, with great love and abnegation, without considering the social condition or the education of these sick, thinking only of curing them or of giving them the hope of a prompt recovery. The costliest medicines were given to them freely, the same as the care of the doctors and the nurses. And as if what was done on the ship were nothing at all, we have seen these same doctors and nurses spreading their goodness in the slums, giving milk to the undernourished children and carrying out wide-scale vaccination programs. Others attended numerous patients in Belén Hospital and performed difficult surgical operations. Faraway cities, such as Piura, Chiclayo, Arequipa, and others, have received visits from the doctors of the *Hope*, and there, before students and doctors alike, gave talks and technical demonstrations with the same unselfishness and goodwill which they had already shown so well in Trujillo.

And now I ask, would it be possible to carry out such a gigantic campaign of goodness and help without possessing an ideal that strengthens the will to noble effort and sacrifice, without being convinced that it is time well employed which is dedicated to assisting one's fellow beings? Those great sacrifices presuppose a high ideal, and such is the case of our friends of the *Hope*. The teaching of the parable of the Good Samaritan has penetrated deeply into their consciousness and has made them understand that to do good to needy fellow beings, to wipe their tears and to calm their sufferings, is a command of the Law of God which must be fulfilled. . . .

This enterprise of the *Hope* must not disappear without a trace when the ship lifts anchor in Salaverry on the 28th. It has given us a great lesson and we must learn it. To imitate it in all its magnitude would be impossible, since we neither have nor hope to have the resources which could compare with theirs. But what we can and ought to imitate is that preoccupation for the well-being of our neighbors, for our brothers in need, especially for the sick. For that we shall be able to count on for some time to come with the cooperation of some of the doctors and nurses of the *Hope* who shall remain among us. In order to carry out their plans they have confidence in the Committee which I have the honor to head, and we trust in the help of all those who have understood that we must give something of our own to alleviate the sufferings of others. Out of the generosity of great and small will depend the success of our task of helping others.

And now, doctors and nurses of the *Hope*, as president of the Committee of Aid to the Project HOPE, which has organized this overflowing tribute, I am going to make the presentation of the Commemorative Album of the gratitude of this nation toward you. Here you have 10,000 signatures, from the great to the lowliest, testimony to their gratitude for health recovered, or to their admiration for a work well done. We ask you to place this album in an honored place on the ship, so that, wherever you may go in the future, everyone shall know that here is a nation that has received benefits from you and that has known how to thank you sincerely and affectionately, that this land, this city is Trujillo, in Peru, the same people who have gathered here today round about you, in order to bid you farewell and to desire for you a prosperous pilgrimage throughout the seas of the world, seeking for people who need help. We hope that they know how to understand as well as we do this wonderful gesture of charity.

At the conclusion of his speech, the archbishop presented us with the beautifully bound leather volume containing the signatures of the citizens of Trujillo, which they had been preparing for weeks, and now one of our most prized possessions.

Archie Golden replied on our behalf, for his Spanish was the best on our staff. He later told me that this had been the greatest thrill of his life. His remarks were greeted with resounding cheers at the end of each sentence, and I believe on that day in February he could have been elected Mayor of Trujillo. It was not so much what he said, but rather that he spoke to the people of Trujillo in their own language, and they accepted this as a binding gesture of friendship.

Following this, we really began the countdown. We stopped admitting patients to the ship, and ward by ward closed down the ship's hospital. Surgery was shut down three days before scheduled departure, and the last patient was sent ashore forty-eight hours later. The ship began to take on a ghostly quality, and everyone became uncomfortable. Those girls who were not going with us to Ecuador were packing trunks, and ponchos and sombreros were stacked throughout the passageways. Except for the hospital levels, which were now quiet and empty, the ship was almost like a tourist vessel, and seemed completely out of character. Many loose ends were still to be tied taut ashore. A fair amount of supplies had to be stored for our shore-based group that was to remain. Last-minute visits to the clinics, patients, and friends were completed. The whole community seemed as saddened as were we on the ship.

On the night before departure, the thousands of Peruanos who wished to say "good-bye HOPE" began to pour into

Trujillo. There were Indians who had come hundreds of miles from the sierra because we had repaired a child's cleft palate or made a blind *campesino*'s vision return. Others came from Lima, Arequipa, Talara, and many other cities. Lord only knows where they slept, for they could not be absorbed by either Salaverry or Trujillo.

As night fell, more than ten thousand already lined the beach and began a tremendous fireworks display. There were bands and wandering groups of musicians playing the national songs of both countries. On board the *Hope* there was little we could do in return except cheer, and pray that they heard us. Finally Frank Quattlebaum, a surgeon from Minneapolis, went up on the bridge and answered each salvo from the shore with a blast from our ship's whistle. We set up a loudspeaker, and some of the girls sang choruses from the songs they had prepared for our own ship's show. They must have been heard, because the songs received loud rounds of applause.

The evening seemed endless until we heard a tremendous blast from the beach. It was the finale of the fireworks presentation, and skyrockets of every color and design filled the starlit heavens. Coupled with the loud roar of amazement at the beauty onshore were some unmistakable screams of horror. The very worst had happened. An evening of celebration was to end in tragedy. I turned immediately to Fernando Cabieses, who was on board with us, and he answered my question before I could ask it:

"Someone is seriously hurt, Bill. You had better get surgery ready. They will bring them out here!"

I issued the orders, and the girls, only a moment before exhilarated and relaxed, turned to and headed for surgery. One ward had been left made up in the event of crew or staff illness on the way home, so we were all right there. As I turned toward the beach, the crowd stood in a stunned silence. The sound of the *Rosita's* motor and Othello's shrill bark brought the message across the intervening water loud and clear. Casualties were coming.

Cabby hurriedly explained to me that to ensure that the final display in a fireworks show have a loud and colorful explosion, it was the custom to pile rocks around the explosives and set the skyrockets in the middle. He went on: "Occasionally the explosives will detonate sideways instead of upward, and if this is what has happened several people must have been struck by large pieces of flying rock. In a crowd as large as this one, there is no telling how many have been hurt."

As he finished talking we had reached the sea gangway, and as we looked down the boatman was yelling, "Siete, siete." Even in the poor light the seven resembled a boatload of war casualties. Blood was everywhere, and the injured had to be brought on board in stretchers. Only a very few minutes had elapsed since the blast, and as I turned around I noticed the on-call nurses in uniform and ready for work. Eileen Murphy and Shirley Johnson reported the operating rooms ready, and Ann Roden and Dorothy Aeschliman led us to the ward. It was as if the ship had never closed down its hospital operation.

A girl of twenty lay completely unconscious. Her black hair had fallen over a beautiful young face, ashen and expressionless. Her excited companions explained that a piece of flat rock had flown almost sixty feet and struck her in the chest, just over the heart, and she had dropped to the ground without a sound. No sign of any injury could be seen, and yet there were no heart sounds, no blood pressure, and no discernible respiration. Dr. Leo, a cardiologist from Long Island, and I worked on her as rapidly as possible. External cardiac massage, oxygen, and all other emergency measures failed. We did not want to believe she was dead when she arrived, but dead she was—a tragic end to what began as an evening of celebration.

Only the ever-present Father Magner was able to help her as he quietly carried out the ritual of the last rites.

A second casualty, a man of about forty, was covered with blood, and unconscious. It was obvious that the front of his skull had been smashed in by the flying rocks. I turned to Cabby and asked him if he would operate, since our neurosurgeon had already left the ship for home. "Of course," he replied, and turning to Frank Quattlebaum, a general surgeon, to ask his assistance, the two of them headed for surgery.

The other five were more bloody than serious, although two had sufficient blood loss to require transfusions. The blood came from our own staff, a final gesture forging a link between friends.

Almost three hours later a haggard Cabby, together with the rest of the surgical team, returned from surgery. Looking at me through eyes red with fatigue and strain, Cabby said, "He'll live, Bill."

It was almost 4:00 A.M. before the ward was quieted down and relatives put ashore. The ship had become a fully functioning hospital in a matter of minutes; the instincts of our staff enabled them to react beautifully. None of us will ever forget the skilled and steady hands of Fernando Cabieses. It was a night to remember with pride as well as sorrow.

We wondered how the tragedy would affect our departure the next day. We knew the women of the town, under the chairmanship of Marcella de Ganoza, had been working for weeks in preparation; they wanted to start decorating the ship at 6:00 A.M. Most of us did not bother to go to bed at all, for the patients would have to be moved ashore before the crowds gathered.

As the sun rose from out of the sea behind us, I walked out on deck to find Marcella and her committee already at work, trimming the ship from stem to stern with colorful flowers that had been individually attached to long strings of wire. Colored paper streamers flowed in the early breeze from every mast and railing. Signs were suspended over the side saying *Adiós Amigos*. People were again gathering on the beaches and the pier; cars and wagons already filled the road to Salaverry, and clouds of sand billowed up as they came almost bumper to bumper.

By seven, the military band was playing, and its brassy tones brought out even those who had tried to get some sleep after the long night just passed. Our two launches began to bring friends and former patients to the ship. The archbishop came with his biretta perched on the back of his head, and smiled down at his grateful flock. The tears that flowed, both gringo and Peruano, could have floated the ship. Everyone, from the poorest to the wealthiest, brought a token with him, and the problems of the customs officers in New York were multiplied a hundredfold in one morning. The crowd on the shore swelled by the thousands, and since most could not board the *Hope,* they shouted for their friends. We sent our nurses out on the launch in small groups so that they could ride close to the pier, which was now a solid mass of humanity. Some were crying, others laughing, but each had brought a flower. As the launch went by, the people shouted to their favorites and threw them flowers until the *Rosita* looked like a floating greenhouse. This was repeated time and time again, and I wondered how much more emotion these wonderful women could take.

Two hours before sailing time, the crowd had swelled to forty thousand. The beaches as far down as one could see were covered with a tightly packed mob out to show their affection to the formerly despised Yanqui. As the last launch load of visitors left the ship, an almost unbelievable quiet descended. It was broken only by occasional sobbing, and then suddenly by a flight of Peruvian Air Force jets that flew back and forth overhead several times in their tribute to a gallant crew.

At 2:00 P.M. Captain Elijah Howe blew a farewell blast with the ship's whistle, the screws turned, and the *Hope* slowly began to slide out of Salaverry harbor. My moments of reflection interrupted by the blast, I looked at Cabby, who was unashamedly weeping. We embraced in the custom so common to the countries south of us, and then turned to watch the masses on shore. They waved, but no one left his spot, and as the ship sailed over the horizon, forty thousand silent people watched. Not a cloud of a dust was raised; not a soul left until the good ship *Hope* sailed out of sight.

[17]

Cabby was sailing to the United States with us. He had been asked to appear before a special luncheon being given for the members of the House of Representatives Foreign Affairs Committee. They wanted to know what HOPE meant to Peru, and they wanted to hear it from a Peruvian. I avoided discussing Cabby's impending testimony with him, but I myself was anxious to know what he would say. It was important that all of us involved in HOPE know whether we were right or wrong in what we tried to do. I had seen Cabby in the operating room only the night before; I knew he was a man of coolness and courage. I knew, too, he would think carefully before he spoke. We of HOPE were soon to return to Ecuador. Cabby's words would have much to do with the attitude toward our next mission.

On March 15, 1963, Cabby made his statement. To an attentive luncheon hosted by Congressman Ed Edmonson of Oklahoma, he told first of the overwhelming sendoff given HOPE by the people of Trujillo. He recounted our achievements—medical, sociological, political, personal—in flattering detail. He analyzed the difficulties of the Latin American when confronted with the "real Yankee" as opposed to his dreary image. He made clear that industry alone could not solve his country's economic problems. With some trepidation, I heard him put to the Committee members the rhetorical question

"Are health programs an investment or an expense?" and awaited his answer.

. . . Any program which creates in a group the idea that the health of its people is the responsibility of others, or that their well-being is a grant they should expect and demand from somebody else, is suicidal. A program of this sort, whether it is for health, housing, land reform or any other social aim, becomes not only a dangerous expense—it is a sociological crime.

But when you find that health needs serve as a starting point for free communication between two peoples; when you see that health programs can be so effectively used as a starter for the development of higher motivations; when one can easily prove that health programs become a tool for linking two different cultures; then, every cent spent within this framework is worth a dollar. And I would call this an investment, and a very good one!

I have bitterly criticized many of the health, nutritional, and educational programs which are now being carried out in Latin America, both within the Alliance framework or independently by our national governments. I have done so because in their operation they are missing the most essential characteristics of a true development program. Many of them are giveaway, handout deals, based on fifteenth-century charity. Many are paternalistic, morally degrading, and leading only to dependence, easy living, and lack of individual responsibility.

If they have any effect at all, they will end in state control of all human needs, they will kill free enterprise, and will finally take us all where nobody in the Alliance wants to go.

In many instances, this is done out of sheer ignorance. Other times, this road is chosen because it is the easiest to organize. But most of the time, these programs are the unadulterated product of political shortsightedness. Local politicians who find an easy way to obtain popularity with the money and work of others.

Here is where we come to the very ticklish question of the leader image.

Assuming we agree that the U.S.A. is the leader of this Alliance. Assuming we agree that the programs which most

appeal to the soul of Latin American people are those directed
to fill the basic human needs. Assuming that these programs
are kept on a sociologically sound basis for development of
local resources, I leave it for you to decide whether your own
people should or should not be given the opportunity personally to participate in the difficult task of organizing and leading
at least part of these programs. I leave it for you to decide
whether the little man with his burro and the poor tamale
vendor should be given the opportunity personally to meet the
people who are making this program possible. I leave it for
you to decide whether the Alliance itself may or may not risk
missing an opportunity to enhance the leader image in programs that really reach the heart of the people. And I leave it
for you to decide whether you want your people to continue
hiding under a dollar sign or you want them to show their real
faces to their Latin American friends.

Project HOPE has shown the way in Trujillo, Peru. The S.S.
Hope has returned to the United States after a ten months'
successful mission—and it has left behind there, as it did in
Indonesia and Vietnam, a true legacy of learning, a real people-
to-people communication. Project HOPE has served Americans
well, and the people of Peru will not forget their friends.

CONCLUSION

Cabby finished, and the room was silent. I felt very proud. Proud of our Project, proud of its mission, but proudest of all of its people. Those who had served with us in Peru, who had indeed crossed new frontiers. This was more than healing the sick and teaching others. It was the very willingness of people to leave a land of plenty to go to a strange land; to do what their hearts tell them must be done; to work a seven-day week and a day without end; to go to the edge of the desert, to the tops of mountains, and into the denseness of the jungles, and do it willingly. It was this spirit of these people that counted most.

Their greatest asset was their heritage. They were Americans. They were asked only to remember this and to act as good Americans. The world has become a large battlefield, not so much for arms as for ideas and ideals. Every American abroad is a target for alien philosophy. Every advantage is taken of any mistake we make. These men and women did not make many mistakes; and more, they demonstrated that the United States is a nation with a heart.

It was the Peruvian pilot who told our skipper as he was leaving the ship outside Salaverry: "Tell your countrymen not to send money to Latin America. It is wasted. Tell them to send people, people like the Hopies, for this reaches our people. . . . Look at the thousands of people on the shore— there is living proof. They have been deeply touched by the *Hope,* their lives changed. Tell them to send us more ships of Hope."

EPILOGUE

The record of HOPE's achievement in Peru by no means ceased on the day the ship weighed anchor in 1963. Since then, HOPE has continued to maintain a team of teachers at the Hospital School for Teaching and Training at the University of Trujillo. There, thanks to the continuing cooperation and affection of the Peruvian people, successes beyond any we could have dreamed of have been achieved, both at the old Belén Hospital as well as the new Hospital for Teaching and Training affiliated with the medical school. Today we feel that this hospital is the equivalent of any hospital of comparable size in the United States. Department by department they have adopted new concepts of teaching and new techniques, spreading the reputation of the hospital throughout Peru and the neighboring countries of South America.

Jorge de Vinatea, who was the courageous spirit behind the early cooperation with HOPE in Trujillo, has since been elected Dean of the Medical School by his colleagues. The students are our warm friends, and by raising their sights have strengthened the university immeasurably. They are participating not only in the clinics surrounding Trujillo, but also have indicated strong interest in sending graduate volunteers to work in the jungles of the Amazon to help make President Belaunde's dream come true.

In 1965 a nursing school was begun in Trujillo with the help of our own devoted teachers. We at HOPE no longer feel like strangers in a foreign land, for the Peruvian people now welcome us as their own, and will continue to welcome anyone who helps them to help themselves.

The S.S. *Hope* itself has since early 1963 completed missions in Ecuador, in the Republic of Guinea, and most recently has brought her devoted staff to the Republic of Nicaragua. The staff may change, but the strength of our communion with others continues, for as Diogenes has said: Hope is the dream of a waking man. We live today in an awakening world, and we help give to others the possibility of fulfilling their dreams because we believe in one another.

HONOR ROLL

Abrams, Bernard S., M.D., Ohio
Abrams, Stanley D., Maryland
Adamcin, Donna, Ohio
Adams, Harold R., M.D., Minnesota
Adams, La Vera, Iowa
Adams, John, M.D., California
Adler, Denis C., M.D., California
Aeschliman, Dorothy, California
Agner, Drexel E., California
Aguilera, Gloria, New York
Ahern, Elizabeth, Wisconsin
Albrecht, Robert M., M.D., New York
Alcorn, Marshall, M.D., Michigan
Allende, Manuel F., M.D., California
Alvarez, Loretta E., M.D., Philippines
Amromin, George D., M.D., California
Anderson, D. I., D.D.S., California
Anderson, E. Patricia, Florida
Anderson, Frederick, M.D., Connecticut
Anderson, Howard S., D.D.S., Washington
Anderson, Ruth, New York
Angland, Thomas A., M.D., Washington
Anna, Wm. P., Jr., Rev., Maryland
Antell, Gunnard J., M.D., Florida
Arnhold, Rainer G., M.D., California
Austermiller, Joan, Michigan

Baiz, Theodore C., M.D., Virginia
Baker, Thomas J., M.D., Florida
Bamford, Joel M., New York
Baptisti, Arthur, Jr., M.D., Indiana
Baptisti, Nan, Indiana
Barclay, C. G., M.D., Idaho
Barden, Stewart P., M.D., Michigan
Barker, Lowell J., New York
Barnes, Roger W., M.D., California
Barton, Lewis, M.D., New York
Beahm, Michael R., Virginia
Beaubien, Mark S., M.D., Michigan
Bendler, Eleanor M., M.D., Pennsylvania
Benner, A. Morton, M.D., California
Bergman, R. Theodore, M.D., California
Bernard, K. Irene, Maryland
Berry, Elizabeth, Connecticut
Best, Dorothy, New Mexico
Besterman, Elaine, Ohio
Bezman, Alyce, M.D., California
Bianchi, Jennie L., New York
Billett, Anthony E., D.D.S., Ohio
Billimek, Marilyn, Texas
Bingham, Harvey D., M.D., Washington
Birdsall, Barbara L., California
Bishop, Isabel, Michigan
Black, Ethel A., California
Black, Rita, Colorado

Blanton, Frederick M., M.D., Florida
Bloom, Herbert J., D.D.S., Michigan
Bock, Rudolph, M.D., California
Bodner, Henry, M.D., California
Boehme, Earl J., M.D., California
Bowen, Leon M., Virginia
Bowen, Mrs. Leon M., (Charlotte Roller), Virginia
Boyce, Lois, California
Boyle, Mary, Michigan
Bradbury, Betty Ann, Virginia
Bradley, Nancy, Oregon
Brannon, Mrs. Marianne Rawack, California
Braun, Harold A., M.D., Montana
Brenan, Margaret, Pennsylvania
Brennan, Patricia A., M.D., Missouri
Bridges, Joyce, North Carolina
Briggs, John N., M.D., California
Brinley, Floyd J., Jr., M.D., Maryland
Brooks, Harold W., M.D., Kansas
Brown, Joan, West Virginia
Brown, John Q., M.D., Ohio
Brown, Marvin, M.D., Ohio
Brown, Robert E., New Jersey
Brown, Roy E., M.D., New York
Bryan, Burton D., M.D., Massachusetts
Bull, Leland, M.D., Washington
Burchett, Dorothy, Missouri
Burgdorf, C. P. M., Jos., Rev. New York
Burnett, Richard C., M.D., California
Burns, Robert E., M.D., Michigan
Burns, William, M.D., Pennsylvania

Cairns, Lottie Reich (Mrs. Andrew), Arizona
Campana, Joseph F., M.D., Pennsylvania
Campbell, Anson B., District of Columbia
Campbell, Teresa Mary, California
Campion, Ann T., (Nancy), Connecticut
Campion, Mary, Minnesota
Capriotti, Octavius A., M.D., Pennsylvania
Carlson, Betty, Washington
Carr, Seymour Joseph D., M.D., California
Carter, Dolores, California
Cattoni, Martin, D.D.S., Texas
Chace, Richard, D.D.S., Florida
Chaffin, Ruth I. (Mrs. Douglas Sage), California
Chamberlain, Naomi, New York
Chandler, Arthur C., M.D., West Virginia
Chase, Gerard, M.D., California

Cheney, Linda, Massachusetts
Cherney, Paul J., M.D., Pennsylvania
Childs, Alfred W., M.D., California
Chrest, Clarence P., M.D., Michigan
Chu, Fred Chin, New Jersey
Clark, Edith S., New York
Clark, Elizabeth A., M.D., Vermont
Clark, H. Ford, M.D., Pennsylvania
Class, Robert N., M.D., Arizona
Clendenin, Marge, Maryland
Clifford, Othnile, Ohio
Coffelt, Carl F., M.D., California
Cohen, Martin, M.D., Arizona
Coley, Geoffrey M., M.D., Connecticut
Collier, June, California
Combs, Mildred, North Carolina
Cook, Dorothy, Canada
Cook, Sharon, Michigan
Cook, V. Valerie, Michigan
Cooke, Samuel L., M.D., Kentucky
Cooper, Alan J., M.D., Washington
Corley, Charles, M.D., California
Coulter, William H., M.D., Iowa
Covalt, Nila K., M.D., Florida
Coventry, Mark B., M.D., Minnesota
Cramer, Fritz, M.D., New York
Crary, Mary Jo Ann, Utah
Craven, Renee, Michigan
Craw, Nicholas W., District of Columbia
Cress, William, M.D., California
Crosswhite, Vivian, Ohio
Curtis, Charles P., Jr., M.D., Connecticut
Custer, Frederic, D.D.S., Pennsylvania
Czerapowicz, Carol A., Massachusetts

Dachi, Stephen F., D.M.D., Kentucky
Damuth, Mary Jane, New York
Daniel, Grace, North Carolina
Daniel, William A., Jr., M.D., Alabama
Daut, R. V., M.D., Iowa
Day, Mary, California
DeBelius, Lawrence, California
Decker, Harold A., M.D., Ohio
Decker, John P., M.D., Pennsylvania
Deeths, Harry J., M.D., California
Dehlinger, Klaus, M.D., California
Del Giorno, Thomas, M.D., Michigan
DeLuz, Mrs. Kristena E., California
Dempsey, Charlotte, New York
Dennis, Harold S., M.D., California
Dennis, Robert L., M.D., California
deSelva, Violette B., District of Columbia
DeVoe, Robert W., M.D., California
DiBona, Janet, Massachusetts
Dickerson, Charles, Michigan
Dickey, Pauline, Ohio
Dickson, W. B., M.D., New York
Digges, Maria N., Maryland
Doane, Joseph C., M.D., Florida
Donahue, Margaret M., Michigan
Donley, Joan M., Ohio
Donnelly, Sally, Pennsylvania
Donovan, Sarah, Ohio
Dorame, Delia, California
Doyle, Barbara, Connecticut
Drinker, Anne S., M.D., Pennsylvania
Drosd, Rudolph E., M.D., Florida
Duerksen, Merlyn C., M.D., California
Dunlap, Edward A., M.D., New York
Dunn, Philip K., California

Durham, Davis G., M.D., Delaware
Dusenberry, Charles, M.D., New York
Dysart, Benjamin R., M.D., California

Edmunds, David W., Rev., Texas
Edwards, Doris Anne, Pennsylvania
Eiman, John W., M.D., Pennsylvania
Elias, Ralph B., M.D., California
Elliott, Richard O., M.D., Massachusetts
Elliott, Robert, D.D.S., California
Ellis, Eldon, E., M.D., California
Elmore, Mary, Michigan
England, Barbara, North Carolina
Ennis, LeRoy M., D.D.S., Pennsylvania
Enright, James, California
Erickson, Barbara J., Washington
Erickson, Carl A., M.D., California
Etzwiler, Donnel D., M.D., Minnesota

Fager, Charles A., M.D., Massachusetts
Fakkema, LaVerne, California
Falck, Frank J., Ph.D., Vermont
Falck, Vilma, T., Ph.D., Vermont
Farrington, Charles, M.D., Florida
Feeney, Kathleen, Iowa
Feigelson, Howard, M.D., Michigan
Fernbach, L. Virginia, New York
Ferreira, Genevieve, California
Fifer, John S., M.D., Florida
Finley, Mary Ellen, California
Fisher, John J., M.D., Florida
Flanigan, Stevenson, M.D., Connecticut
Fleuchaus, Philip T., D.D.S., Florida
Folcik, Pauline, Michigan
Folger, William S., M.D., California
Folsom, Clarence H., M.D., California
Foltz, Mary Louise, Pennsylvania
Fooks, Doris, Kentucky
Foote, C. M., M.D., Nebraska
Footer, Wilson, M.D., California
Forsythe, Paul J., Rev., Virginia
Foti, Ignatia, New York
Fountain, Edmund M., M.D., Texas
Franzblau, M. J., M.D., California
Frevert, Elaine, District of Columbia
Friedman, Eugene, D.D.S., New York
Fritz, Doris Anne, District of Columbia

Gaiser, Judith F., District of Columbia
Gallagher, Mary L., California
Gallagher, William B., M.D., Wisconsin
Garson, C. H., D.D.S., California
Gass, H. Harvey, M.D., Michigan
Geraci, Charles L., M.D., California
Gerber, Alex, M.D., California
Gerber, Edward, M.D., California
Geuting, Joseph T., III, Maryland
Gianotti, E. F., M.D., California
Gibson, Henry H., M.D., Ohio
Gingles, Carle E., D.D.S., Michigan
Glocke, Susan B., California
Glover, Mary A., M.D., Hawaii
Goble, Joan H., M.D., California
Goble, John L., M.D., California
Goiney, Bernard J., M.D., Washington
Golden, Archie S., M.D., Connecticut
Golden, Sylvia (Mrs. Archie S.), Connecticut
Goler, George G., M.D., Ohio
Goodwin, Bonnie E., Michigan
Gordon, Harold N., M.D., Arizona
Gordon, Howard L., M.D., Florida

Kohner, Dinah, M.D., Northern Ireland
Kramer, Bernard M., M.D., California
Krauss, Audrey, M.D., Pennsylvania
Kremer, Howard U., M.D., Pennsylvania
Kremer, William F., M.D., New York
Krol, Mary Ann, Illinois
Kron, Samuel D., M.D., Pennsylvania
Krueger, Carol, Illinois
Kuharic, Henry, M.D., Washington
Kuhn, Mark A. R., M.D., Florida
Kushwara, Barbara, Pennsylvania
Kyle, Sally C., Massachusetts

Lack, Herbert, M.D., California
Lally, Timothy F., M.D., California
Lamphere, Lottie, Michigan
Langer, Catherine, Illinois
Langston, J. D., M.D., Michigan
La Rose, Joseph, W.F., New Jersey
Lawler, Dolores, New York
Lawrence, Montague, M.D., Iowa
Layman, Mary, California
leBrocquy, Jean, M.D., Ireland
LeCheminant, Wilford H., M.D., Utah
LeCocq, John F., M.D., Washington
Lehmann, J. H., M.D., Washington
Leland, Carol M., M.D., California
Leman, Craig, M.D., Oregon
Lenel, Rosemarie M., M.D., California
Lentino, Walter, M.D., New York
Leo, Thomas F., M.D., New York
Lesko, Geraldine, California
Lesko, Louis, M.D., California
Liebowitz, Daniel, M.D., California
Liechty, R. D., M.D., Iowa
Linden, Jack L., M.D., New York
Lindley, Sheldon K., M.D., California
Lipsey, James H., Jr., M.D., Tennessee
Lloyd, Stacy B, District of Columbia
Loehning, Robert, M.D., Utah
Long, Albert E., M.D., California
Longman, Alice J., New York
Lowry, Robert A., M.D., Michigan
Ludwig, Ninalee H., Kentucky
Lukasik, Claudette, Wisconsin
Lutz, Velma, Ohio
Luz, Lester A., M.D., California

Macgregor, Charles A., M.D., Massachusetts
Mack, Elaine E., Ohio
Madison, James B., M.D., Florida
Magner, John F., Rev., S.J., California
Malik, Nancy, California
Manion, Ruth, California
Manwell, Edward J., M.D., Massachusetts
March, Harriet Seipel, California
Margold, Allen M., M.D., Connecticut
Margolis, Alan J., M.D., California
Mark, Joseph P., M.D., California
Mark, Richard S., New York
Marks, Richard M., M.D., California
Martin, Joan, Kansas
Martin, S. Lawrence, Jr., District of Columbia
Mason, Thomas H., M.D., New York
Mathewson, Eleanor, California
Matteis, Joice, Connecticut
Matthews, B. Ellen, District of Columbia
Mayall, Stanley E., D.D.S., Washington
McBratney, J. Greer, M.D., Massachusetts
McBride, Robert H., M.D., Iowa

McCannel, Macolm, M.D., Minnesota
McClintock, Robert S., M.D., California
McCort, James, M.D., California
McCutcheon, Sue A., M.D., Michigan
McConnell, Bernie A., D.D.S., Ohio
McConnell, Dona, Ohio
McDermott, John, M.D., California
McDonald, Jean, California
McDonald, William, M.D., Montana
McDonnell, D. P., M.D., California
McDonough, John, Ohio
McIntyre, Eleanor C., Michigan
McKinney, Brenda, North Carolina
McKinney, Frederick M., Illinois
McLaren, H. J., M.D., Pennsylvania
McLean, Ronald, California
McMurry, Bryce E., M.D., Washington
McQuigg, Ronald W., M.D., Ohio
McQuillan, Marjorie, Washington
Mead, Peyton, M.D., Connecticut
Mella, Barbara A., M.D., Michigan
Mendelsohn, Harvey, M.D., Ohio
Metcalf, Malcolm, Iowa
Miller, Alexander, M.D., Ohio
Miller, Barbara, Pennsylvania
Miller, John S., M.D., California
Miller, William W., M.D., California
Millett, John F., D.D.S., New York
Mirata, Nancy, California
Misuraca, Leroy A., M.D., California
Mitchell, Mancel T., M.D., Minnesota
Monti, Jay, Pennsylvania
Mooney, Cecelia, Oregon
Moore, Robert L., D.D.S., Georgia
Morris, Kenneth A., M.D., Florida
Morris, Marlyn, Colorado
Morrison, Carolyn, New York
Morrow, Dorothy, M.D., Vermont
Morrow, Paul L., Vermont
Morrow, Robert C., Vermont
Morrow, Rufus C., M.D., Vermont
Mount, Lester A., M.D., New York
Mudge, Florence, California
Munton, Mary, New York
Murphy, Ann M., New York
Murphy, Catherine, Connecticut
Murphy, Eileen, Massachusetts
Musset, Gerald, Colorado
Myers, Philip R., M.D., California
Myers, T. R., M.D., California

Nagel, Harry T., M.D., Illinois
Nash, Henry H., M.D., Washington
Nation, Earl F., M.D., California
Neal, Richard M., Jr., Tennessee
Needell, Mervin H., M.D., Florida
Nelson, Marjorie, M.D., Pennsylvania
Nichols, Ervin F., M.D., California
Nixon, Robert K., M.D., Michigan
Noble, Andrew, M.D., California
Norstrom, Shirley A., Minnesota
Nussbaum, Martha J., Tennessee

O'Bear, Margaret, M.D., New York
Oblender, John, California
O'Brien, Anne, Massachusetts
O'Connor, Marcella, California
Ogle, Ben C., Jr., M.D., North Carolina
Oglesby, Richard B., M.D., Missouri
O'Grady, Roberta S., California
Oliver, Dalton S., M.D., Louisiana
O'Neil, Claire E., New York
Orbeton, Everett A., M.D., Maine

Smith, Ransan L., M.D., Washington
Smith, Robert G., M.D., Ohio
Smith, Veronica, Pennsylvania
Smoller, Arnold J., M.D., New York
Snow, Donald L., Maryland
Snyder, Howard McCrum, III, Georgia
Sontos, Alexander, New Jersey
Soto, Anita, Ph.D., Florida
Sobeck, Frederick J., M.D., California
Soule, Elizabeth, North Carolina
Southwick, Wayne O., M.D., Connecticut
Spangler, Paul E., M.D., California
Spar, Arthur A., M.D., California
Sperelakis, Nick, Ph.D., Ohio
Spreckelmyer, Marylouise, Indiana
Springer, Joe P., M.D., Wisconsin
Staatz, Dumont S., M.D., Washington
Stack, Robert E., M.D., Minnesota
Stafford, C. E., M.D., California
Staples, Albert F., D.M.D., Texas
Steadman, Rodger C., Pennsylvania
Steele, Jeffrey L., District of Columbia
Steiner, Joan, Kansas
Stern, C. A., M.D., South Dakota
Stevens, Alexander R., Jr., M.D., Washington
Stewart, H. C., M.D., Nebraska
Stewart, John E., M.D., Washington
Stocker, Harold H., M.D., California
Stoll, Carolyn, Michigan
Storkan, Margaret A., M.D., California
Straub, Daniel L., M.D., California
Strauss, Arnold, M.D., Virginia
Stringer, Barbara, Michigan
Strong, Caroline L., Maryland
Strong, Priscilla, Connecticut
Stubenbord, John G., M.D., New York
Sweet, Patricia, Massachusetts
Swendson, James J., M.D., Minnesota

Tarcher, Alyce Bezman, M.D., California
Taren, James A., M.D., Michigan
Tegenkamp, Irene E., Mrs., Ohio
Terry, John L., M.D., Ohio
Tetirick, Jack E., M.D., Ohio
Thomas, Merle, M.D., Texas
Thomas, William N., Jr., M.D., Maryland
Thompson, Jack E., M.D., California
Thompson, Richard C., M.D., California
Thompson, Sally, Ohio
Till, Harry J., M.D., Alabama
Tilney, Robert W., Jr., M.D., New Jersey
Tisher, Paul W., M.D., Connecticut
Tocantins, Ronald, M.D., Washington
Toth, Robert J., Maryland
Townsend, Jean, New York
Tracy, Charles J., Minnesota
Tremblay, Louise, New Hampshire
Troland, Charles E., M.D., Virginia
Trowbridge, F. L., Ohio
Tucker, Charles E., M.P.H., Kentucky
Tucker, Grace, Massachusetts
Turner, Thomas A., M.D., Kansas
Tyrer, A. Roy, Jr., M.D., Tennessee

Underwood, Rex J., M.D., Oregon

Vande Bunte, Ethel, Michigan
Vandergriff, Katherine, Tennessee
Van Meier, William, Michigan
Vedder, J. S., M.D., Wisconsin
Vettoretti, Johana O., New York
Villegas, Oscar, D.D.S., Michigan

Visser, J. Hugh, M.D., California
Voltz, Vernon C., M.D., Illinois

Waite, Daniel, D.D.S., Minnesota
Walker, James C., M.D., Massachusetts
Walker, Philip H., M.D., Massachusetts
Wall, D. D., M.D., Texas
Wallace, Evelyn G., M.D., California
Waller, John I., M.D., Kansas
Walsh, John, District of Columbia
Walsh, Thomas S., District of Columbia
Walsh, William B., M.D., District of Columbia
Walsh, William B., Jr., District of Columbia
Ward, Helen, North Carolina
Ward, Jennie, Washington
Watkins, Anne, M.D., California
Wawro, N. William, M.D., Connecticut
Wayne, J. Paul, M.D., California
Weaver, Donald G., Iowa
Weaver, Samuel, M.D., California
Webb, Gilbert A., M.D., California
Weber, Maurice, Florida
Webster, Dorothy, Massachusetts
Weed, Chester A., M.D., Connecticut
Weed, Jeffrey, Connecticut
Weeter, John C., M.D., Kentucky
Weeter, John M., Kentucky
Wehrle, Julie Ann, Pennsylvania
Weinschreider, Mary, Michigan
Weisskopf, Alex, M.D., California
Welch, Ilse D., California
Weller, William J., M.D., California
Wenaas, Elmer J., M.D., Ohio
Wertz, M. B., Virginia
Wessel, Hazel E., Hawaii
Westcott, F. Howard, M.D., New Jersey
Westcott, Georgia (Mrs. F. Howard), New Jersey
Whalen, Thomas, New York
Whelton, James A., M.D., Massachusetts
Whittington, Betty, California
Wieczorowski, Elsie, M.D., Illinois
Wiener, M. F., M.D., New York
Wier, Marion E., M.D., Massachusetts
Wild, Lois, New Jersey
Williams, John E., M.D., Washington
Williams, Katheen, Washington
Williams, Kenneth O., M.D., California
Williamson, William P., M.D., Kansas
Wilson, Katherine B., District of Columbia
Winter, Doris, Pennsylvania
Wohlgemuth, Joan, M.D., District of Columbia
Wood, T. Rodman, M.D., California
Woodward, Charles M., D.D.S., California
Wright, Donald, Wyoming
Wyatt, William M., M.D., Georgia

Yankee, Ronald A., M.D., District of Columbia
Yates, Basil, M.D., Florida
Yates, James E., M.D., California
Youker, James E., M.D., Virginia
Young, Forrest, M.D., California
Young, G. Victoria, M.D., California
Young, Malcom C., M.D., Michigan
Young, Billy G., Jr., Oklahoma

Zeier, Francis G., M.D., Indiana
Zeier, Olga G., Indiana

HONOR ROLL of Contributors-in-Kind to Project HOPE

Abbott Laboratories
Academic Press
Accurate Wire Craft Company
Acme Laboratory Equipment Company
Acousticon International
Adam Wuest, Inc.
Adams Packing Company
Adolph's Ltd.
Advance Floor Machine Company
Aeorplast Corporation
Air Instruments
Air Reduction, Inc.
Air Shields, Inc.
Airkem, Inc.
Alaska Packers' Association
Albers Milling Company
Albion Produce Company, Inc.
Alcon Laboratories, Inc.
Alconox, Inc.
A. E. Alexander & Son
Allan Brothers
Allergan Pharmaceuticals, Inc.
Alltronics-Howard Company
A. S. Aloe Company
Alpha Aromatics, Inc.
Ambco Electronics
Ambrosia Chocolate Company
American Association of Blood Banks
American Bakeries
American Can Corporation
American Cancer Society
American College of Radiology
American Cyanamid Company
American Cystoscope Makers, Inc.
American Dental Association
American Dental Manufacturing Company
American Dental Trade Association
American Food Laboratories, Inc.
American Gelosa Electronics, Inc.
American Home Foods
American Home Products
American Hospital Association
American Hospital Supply Company
American Licorice Company
American Maize Products Company
American Manufacturer's Export Division, Ltd.
American Marine Paint Company
American Medical Association
American Merchant Marine Library
American National Red Cross

American Optical Company
American Pharmaceutical Company
American Radio Relay League
American Silk Sutures, Inc.
American Society of Hospital Pharmacists
American Speedlight Corporation
American Sponge and Chamois Company, Inc.
American Sterilizer Company
American Surgical Trade Association
American Tobacco Company
American Uniform Company
Ames Company, Inc.
A. Paul Amos Warehouse
Ampex-Audio, Inc.
Anchor Hocking Glass Corporation
Anchor Products Company
Angelica Uniform Company
Apple Growers Association
Appleton-Century-Crofts, Inc.
Archer Taylor Drug Company
Ark-Homa Farms Frozen Foods, Inc.
Armour Pharmaceutical Company
Armstrong Cork Company
Armstrong Paint & Varnish Works, Inc.
Amar-Stone Laboratories, Inc.
Arno Adhesive Tapes, Inc.
Arthur Schmidt & Associates
Artichoke Industries, Inc.
Arzol Chemical Company
Associated Box Corporation
Associated Hearing Aid Center
Astatic Corporation
Astra Pharmaceutical Products, Inc.
Atlantic Alloy Industries, Inc.
Atlantic Stamping Company
Atlas Chemical Industries, Inc.
Automatic Business Products
Automatic Seriograph Company
Automation Industries
Avery Label Company
Awrey Bakeries, Inc.
Ayerst Laboratories, Inc.

B. T. Babbitt, Inc.
J. T. Baker Chemical Company
Ball Brothers Company, Inc.
Ballo Thermometer Company
Baltimore Biological Laboratory, Inc.
Baltimore Cold Storage
C. R. Bard, Inc.

Bard-Parker Company, Inc.
Barnes-Hind Pharmaceuticals, Inc.
Bauer & Black
W. A. Baum Company, Inc.
Bausch & Lomb, Inc.
Don Baxter
Baxter Laboratories, Inc.
Beacon Laboratories, Inc.
Beam-Matic Hospital Supply Company
Beattie-Coleman
Beaulieu Vineyard
The Rudolph Beaver Company
Beckman Instruments, Inc.
Becton, Dickinson & Company
Beecham Research Laboratories, Inc.
Bell & Howell Foundation
Beltone Hearing Aid Company
Ben Hill Griffin, Inc.
Berivon Company
Best Coat & Apron Manufacturing Company, Inc.
Best Food
Better Containers Manufacturing Company
James G. Biddle Company
David Bilgore & Company, Inc.
Biochemical Procedures
Biological Research
Bird Corporation
The Birtcher Corporation
The Bishop & Babcock Electronics Company
Blake, Moffitt & Towne Company
S. Blickman, Inc.
Block & Guggenheimer, Inc.
Blue Island Specialty Company, Inc.
Blue Lake Packers, Inc.
Blue Ribbon Growers, Inc.
Blue Star Growers, Inc.
Blumenthal Brothers Chocolate Company
Bolderman Chocolate Company
Bolta Products
Bon Vivant Soups, Inc.
Bond Pickle Company, Inc.
F. E. Booth Company, Inc.
Borden Foods Company
Bordo Products Company
Bowey's, Inc.
Boyle-Midway
Breon Laboratories, Inc.
Brew-Schneider Company
The Brewster Corporation
Brinkman Instruments, Inc.
Bristol Laboratories
Bristol-Meyers Company
Broemmel Pharmaceuticals
Brown & Williamson Company
Brunswick Box Company, Inc.
Brunswick Corporation
Brunswick Laboratories
Buckeye Sugars, Inc.
Budget Uniform Center, Inc.
Buffington Electronics, Inc.
Bumble Bee Seafoods, Inc.
Burdick Equipment Company
Burlington Industries
Burnette Farms Packing Corporation
Burnham & Morrill Company
Burnitol Manufacturing Company
Burroughs Brothers Manufacturing Company
Burroughs Wellcome & Company, Inc.

Burton Manufacturing Company
Burton, Parsons & Company
Busse Hospital Disposables, Inc.
Butterworth, Inc.

Cadillac Gage Company
California Canners & Growers
California Fish Canners Association
California Grape & Tree Fruit League
California & Hawaiian Sugar Refining Corporation
California Marine Curing & Packing Company
California Olive Association
California Packing Corporation
Calley & Currier Company
Campbell Soup Company
Can Go Shippers
Can Pro Company
Canada Dry Corporation
Candy, Chocolate, Confectionery Institute of America
Canned Dairy Products, Inc.
Cantaloupe Advisory Board
Capital Bedding Company, Inc.
Carnation Company
Caroline Freight Carriers Corp.
Cascadian Fruit Shippers
Cascoa Growers
Case Laboratories, Inc.
Cashmere Fruit Exchange
Cashmere Pioneer Growers
L. D. Caulk Company
Cetylite Industries, Inc.
Chalet Suzanne Foods, Inc.
Chandler-Logan, Inc.
Chase Chemical Company
Chattanooga Medicine Company
Chattanooga Pharmacal Company, Inc.
Chelsea Milling Company
Chemway Corporation
Cherokee Products Company
Cherry Growers, Inc.
Cherry Products Sales Corporation
Chesebrough-Ponds, Inc.
Chicopee Mills
Chloraseptic Company, Inc.
Christian Becker
Christian Brothers of California
Chrysler Corporation
Chun King Corporation
CIBA Pharmaceutical Company
Clarin Manufacturing Company
Clay-Adams, Inc.
Cleveland Dental Manufacturing Company
Climax Dental Supply Company, Inc.
Clinton Corn Processing Company
Clyde Krout Company
Codman & Shurtleff, Inc.
Coe Laboratories, Inc.
Coffee Instants, Inc.
Coleman Instruments Corporations
Colgate-Palmolive Company
College of American Pathologists
Columbia Fruit Packers, Inc.
Columbia River Packers Association
Columbia Valley Orchards
Columbian Rope Company
Columbus Dental Manufacturing Company
Columbus Plastic Products, Inc.

Comet Rice Mills
Commercial Solvents Corporation
Committee for the Handicapped
Concannon Vineyard
Congdon Orchards, Inc.
Congoleum-Nairn, Inc.
Consolidated Dairy Products
Consolidated Foods Corporation
Consolidated Laboratories, Inc.
Consolidated Materials Handling
Consolidated Midland Corporation
Contadina Foods
Continental Baking Company
Convertors, Inc.
Co-operative Growers of Okanogan
Coors Porcelain Company
Corbin Farnsworth, Inc.
Corn Products
Cornell-Dubilier Electric Corporation
Corning Glass Works
Cosmos Dental Products, Inc.
Country Gardens, Inc.
The Cove-Craft Company
Cowiche Growers
Creamery Package Manufacturing Company
Crescent Dental Manufacturing Company
Crookes-Barnes Laboratories, Inc.
Crown Surgical Manufacturing Company
Cubberly Fruit Company
Curtis Publishing Company
Curtiss Candy Company
Custom Materials, Inc.
Cutter Laboratories
Cypress Gardens Citrus Products, Inc.

Dade Reagents, Inc.
Dairy Maid Products
Dairy Society International
Dairymen's League Cooperative Association, Inc.
Dairypak Butler, Inc.
Damrow Brothers Company
G. Danz & Sons
Data-Guide, Inc.
F. A. Davis Company
Davis & Geck
H. Davis Sound Equipment
Davol Rubber Company
Defiance Milk Products Company
De Laval Separator Company
R. U. Delaphena & Company
Deming & Gould Company
Dennison Manufacturing Company
Denoyer-Geppert Company
The Denticator Company, Inc.
The Dentists' Supply Company of New York
De Puy Manufacturing Company
Desitin Chemical Company
Desoto Canning Company
The De Vilbiss Company
De Witt Lukens Company
Diamond Fruit Company
Diamond National Corporation
Diamond Walnut Growers, Inc.
Dicarbide Products, Inc.
A. B. Dick Foundation
Dictaphone Corporation
Diebold, Inc.
Dietene Company

Difco Laboratories, Inc.
Distillation Products Industries
Ditmar & Penn, Inc.
Dixie Cup
William Dixon, Inc.
Dole Corporation
Dole Refrigerating Company
Dome Chemicals, Inc.
Doughboy Industries
Dow Chemical Company
Dow Corning Corporation
Dowling Textile Manufacturing Company
The Doyle Pharmaceutical Company
Draper-King Cole, Inc.
Drew Chemical Corporation
Duffy Mott Company
DuKane Corporation
Duke Laboratories, Inc.
Dundas & Foregger Anesthesia Company
Dunham Bush, Inc.
Duo-Dens Products, Inc.
DuPaco, Inc.
E. I. duPont de Nemours & Company, Inc.
Durkee Famous Foods
Duro Paper Bag Manufacturing Co.
Dymo Industries, Inc.

Eastman Kodak Company
Eastman Organic
Eastman Tag & Label Company
Eaton Laboratories
Edgett-Burnham Company
Thomas A. Edison Industries
Edroy Products Company, Inc.
Edward Weck & Company, Inc.
Edwards Dental Supply
Electronic Industries, Inc.
Electronic Teaching Laboratories
E-Mac Dairy Brush Company
J. H. Emerson Company
Emesco Dental Company
Empire Brush Company
Endo Laboratories, Inc.
Englehard Hanovia, Inc.
Enjay Chemical Company
Enterprise Paint Manufacturing Company
Erving Paper Mills
Escalon Packers, Inc.
Eskimo Pie Corporation
Essington Metal Works, Inc.
Ethicon, Inc.
Eugene Fruit Growers Association
Everest & Jennings
Everpure, Inc.
Ex-Cell-O Corporation
Eyeshields Company of Massachusetts

Fairview Packing Company
Falcon Plastics Company
Farrall Instrument Company
Fashion Seal Uniform
The Faultless Rubber Company
Thomas Fazio Laboratories, Inc.
Felice & Perrelli Canning Company
Fels & Company
Fenn Brothers, Inc.
Fiberboard Paper Products Corporation
Fisher Scientific Company
C. B. Fleet Company, Inc.

Flex-Straw Company International
Flint-Eaton Company
Florida Canners Association
Florida Citrus Canners Cooperative
J. A. Folger & Company
Foote Clinic
Foote & Jenks, Inc.
Forbes Serta Products
The Foregger Company, Inc.
Foremost Dairies, Inc.
Forma Scientific, Inc.
Forney Fruit & Produce Company
E. Fougera & Company, Inc.
Franco-Italian Packing Company
M. E. Franks, Inc.
Frank Tea & Spice Company
Franz Manufacturing Company, Inc.
Fraser-Sweatman
R. T. French Company
Frito Company
Frosted Fruit Products
Fruit Dispatch Company
Fruit Growers Service
Fruitvale Canning Sales Company
Furman Canning Company

Gamble-Skogmo, Inc.
Gamlen Chemical Company
Gammie Reed Fruit Company
Gangi Brothers Packing Company
Garrett & Company
GeBauer Chemical Company
Geerpres Wringer, Inc.
Geigy Pharmaceuticals
Gem Canning Company
General Aniline & Film Corporation
General Binding Corporation
General Dynamics Corporation
General Electric
General Foam Plastics Corporation
General Foods Corporation
General Mills, Inc.
General Tire & Rubber Company
Gerber Baby Foods
Germantown Manufacturing Company
The William Getz Corporation
Gilbert Orchards, Inc.
Gillette Laboratories
Girton Manufacturing Company
Gist & Chairs, Inc.
Gleed Cold Storage & Packing Company
B. E. Glich & Sons
The Glidden Company
Globe Industries, Inc.
Gomco Surgical Manufacturing Corporation
Goodell Company
B. F. Goodrich Company
Goodwin Brothers Pallet Company
Gorman-Rupp Industries, Inc.
Helen Grace Candies
W. R. Grace & Company
Grafax Instrument Company
Graham-Field Surgical Company, Inc.
Grason Stadler Company, Inc.
Grass Instrument Company
Grower Shipper Vegetable Association of Central California
Grune & Stratton, Inc.
Guittard Chocolate Company
R. O. Gulden Company

Hafner Publishing Company, Inc.
Hahn Brothers, Inc.
Hallicrafters Company
Hamilton Watch Company
Hanau Engineering Company
Hansen Fruit Company
Harbisons Dairies
Hard Manufacturing Company
Hardman Peck & Company
Harley Soap Company
Harper Brothers
P. E. Harris Company
Harter Packing Company
Hartman-Leddon Company
Harvey Dental Specialty Company
Hawey Dental Supply Company
Hawkeye Pearl Button Company
H. J. Heinz Company
Hennicker Crutch Company
Herculite Protective Fabrics Corp.
Steven K. Herlitz, Inc.
Hermes Plastic Company
Heyer-Schulte Corporation
Hiline Growers Co-op
Hills Bros. Coffee, Inc.
Hiram Walker Company
Hitzel Canning Company
Paul B. Hoeber, Inc.
Hoffman-La Roche, Inc.
Robert B. Holland Company
Holland Laundry, Inc.
Hollister, Inc.
Hollister Canning Company
Hollister-Stier Laboratories
Holly Hill Fruit Products Company, Inc.
Holly Sugar Corporation
The Holter Company
Holtzinger Fruit Company
Honeymoon Products
Honorbilt Products, Inc.
E. Frank Hopkins Co. Inc.
Hopper Laboratories
Hordis Brothers
N. Horowitz & Sons
Hospital Topics
Hudson House, Inc.
H. D. Hudson Manufacturing Company
Hudson Oxygen Therapy Sales Company
Hudson Pulp and Paper Corporation
Hu-Friedy Manufacturing Company
Humboldt Manufacturing Company
G. W. Hume Company
Humko Products
Hungerford Packing Company
W. B. Hunt Company
Hygienic Dental Manufacturing Company
Hy-Grain Electronics Corporation
Hyland Laboratories
Hynson, Westcott & Dunning, Inc.
Hypo Surgical Supply Corporation

Idaho Potato & Onion Commission
Ille Electric Corporation
Illinois Canning Company
Illinois Water Treatment Company
Imperial Chemical Industries, Ltd.
Indian Trail Finer Products
Industrial Acoustic Company, Inc.
Ingersoll-Rand Company
Ingram Pharmaceutical Company

Medelec Laboratories, Inc.
Medical Economics, Inc.
Medical Equipment & Photo Corporation
Meinecke Company
Meirett, Inc.
The Mennen Company
Mercer Glass Works, Inc.
Merchant's Warehouse Company
Merck & Company
Merck, Sharp & Dohme
The William S. Merrell Company
Meyer-Blanke Company
Michigan Sugar Company
Mid-Continent Manufacturing Company
Midtown Meat Company
Midwest American
Midwest Dental Manufacturing Company
Mid-West Producer's Creameries, Inc.
James Millen Manufacturing Company
Miltex Instrument Company
Mine Safety Appliance Company
Minnesota Mining & Manufacturing Company
Minter Brothers Candy
Minute Maid Corporation
Misdem-Frank Corporation
Mitchell Syrup & Preserve Company
Mizzy, Inc.
Mobil Oil Company
Mohawk Bedding Corporation
Monitor Sugar
Moore Business Forms, Inc.
Morgan & Sampson, Inc.
Morningstar-Paisley, Inc.
Morton Salt Company
C. V. Mosby Company
Motion Picture Association of America
The J. Bird Moyer Company, Inc.
V. Mueller & Company
Mutual Apple Growers, Inc.
Mynol Chemical Corporation

Naas Foods, Inc.
The Nachman Corporation
The Nakat Packing Corporation
The Nalge Company, Inc.
Nash Engineering Company
Nashua Corporation
National Biscuit Company
National Canners Association
National Dairy Council
The National Drug Company
National Electric Instrument Company, Inc.
National League for Nursing, Inc.
National Soda Straw Company
National Sugar Refining Company
Neisler Laboratories
Nestle Company, Inc.
Neville Chemical Company
New England Confectionery Company
New England Fish Company
New Eyes for the Needy, Inc.
New Haven Rehabilitation Center
New York Bible Society
New York Port Authority
New York Tuberculosis & Health Association
Nissen Corporation
No Knot Hooks Company

Norcliff Laboratories
North American Pharmacal
North Pacific Canners & Packers, Inc.
North Star Dairy
Northern Fruit Company
Northern Paper Mills
Northwest Canners & Freezers Association
Northwest Packing Company
Norwich Pharmacal Company
Noxema Chemical Company
Nuclear-Chicago Corporation

O. R. Laboratories
Oberti Olive Company
Ocean Spray Cranberries, Inc.
Ohio Chemical & Surgical Equipment Company
Olympic Press
Ophthalmos, Inc.
Oral B. Company
Oregon Fruit Products Company
Organon, Inc.
Orinda Olive Corporation
Ormont Drug & Chemical Company, Inc.
Ortho Pharmaceutical Corporation
Orthopedic Equipment Company, Inc.
Orthopedic Frame Company
Osceola Fruit Distributors
Ostrander X-Ray Specialties
Owens-Corning Fiberglas Corporation
Owens-Illinois, Libbey Division
Owens-Illinois, Kimbell Division
Ox Fibre Brush Company, Inc.
Oxford University Press

Pacific American Fisheries, Inc.
Pacific Fruit & Produce Company
Pacific Olive Company
Pan American Airways
Pan Pacific Fisheries, Inc.
Paper Novelty Company
Paperlynen Company
Parenteral Products
Parke-Davis & Company
Parkell Products, Inc.
Paul F. Beich Company
Pearson Candy Company
Pelton Crane
Penberthy Manufacturing Company
Penham Fruit Company
S. B. Penick & Company
Penta Laboratories, Inc.
Penza Bros.
Pepsi-Cola Company
Peshastin Fruit Growers Association
Pest Control Equipment Company
Pet Milk Company
Pfanstiel Laboratories, Inc.
Charles Pfizer & Company, Inc.
Pharmaseal Laboratories
Phillips-Drucker, Inc.
Phillips Molasses Company
Phillips Petroleum Company
Phillips Products Company, Inc.
Physicians Products Company, Inc.
Pianola, Inc.
Picker X-Ray Corporation
The Pillsbury Company
Bernard A. Pincus Company

Pioneer Rubber Company
Pitman-Moore Company
Planda Packers, Inc.
Plantation Chocolate Company
Plasticraft Corporation
Plough, Inc.
Plymouth Citrus Products Co-op
Polaroid Corporation
A. Ponnock & Sons
Portland Canning Company, Inc.
Positive Identification Company
Potlatch Forests, Inc.
Pragel Portable Incubators, Inc.
Pratt Low Company
Precision Carton Company
Precision Scientific Company
Prentice Packing & Cold Storage
J. A. Preston Company
Prince Michigan Manufacturing Company
Princeville Canning Company
Produce Market
Professional Tape Company, Inc.
Propper Manufacturing Company
Pruefer, Inc.
Psychological Corporation
Pure Gold, Inc.
Purex Corporation, Ltd.
Puritan Compressed Gas Corporation

Quaker City Chocolate & Confectionery
Quaker Export Packing Company
The Quaker Oats Company
Queen Products
Quinton Company

RCA Sales Corporation
RCA Whirlpool Corporation
Racine Glove Company, Inc.
Jules Racine & Company, Inc.
Radiant Manufacturing Corporation
Railway Express Company
Ralston Purina Company
Ramsey Winch
Rayflex Exploration Company
Ray-O-Vac
The Reader's Digest
Real-Kill Products
Red Stack Tow Boat Company
Reed & Carnrick Pharmaceuticals
Refined Syrups & Sugars, Inc.
Reliance Dental Manufacturing Company
Remington Rand International
Reproduction Engineering Corporation
Resiflex Laboratory, Inc.
Resinol Chemical Company
Revell, Inc.
Revlon
Rexall Drug & Chemical Company
Rhoades Rubber Corporation
Richards Manufacturing Company
Richardson & Holland, Inc.
Riker Laboratories
Rinn Corporation
Risser Orthopedic Research
The P. J. Ritter Company
Ritter Pfaudler Corporation
Robertson Photo-Mechanix
A. H. Robins Company, Inc.
John R. Robinson, Inc.

Roche Fruit Company
Rochester Products Company
Rocky Mountain Dental Products Company
Roehr Products Company
Rogers Brothers Company
Rogue River Packing Corporation
Rolando Lumber Company, Inc.
Ronson Corporation
William H. Rorer, Inc.
Raymond Rosen & Co., Inc.
Ross Laboratories
Rubbermaid, Inc.
Rudman & Schofield, Inc.
Rusch, Inc.
Ruson Laboratories, Inc.
Russell Radio Ear Company
Russell Stover Candies
Rust-Oleum Corporation

Safeway Stores, Inc.
Salada Foods, Inc.
Samuel Smith Memorial Public Library
San Francisco Heart Association
San Francisco Port Authority
San Jose Canning Company
San Juan Fishing & Packing Company
San Juan Islands Cannery
Sana Dairies
Sanborn
Sandoz Pharmaceuticals, Inc.
Sanivoid Company
Santa Clara Packing Company
W. B. Saunders Company
Savage Laboratories, Inc.
Scavengers Protective Association
Schafer Bakeries, Inc.
Schenley Industries, Inc.
R. P. Scherer Corporation
Schering Corporation
Schick X-Ray Company
Schieffelin & Company
Frank Scholz X-Ray Corporation
Schukl & Company
Schweppes, USA, Ltd.
Scientific Apparatus Makers Association
Scientific Products
Joseph E. Seagram & Sons, Inc.
Sealright Company, Inc.
Sealtest Foods
G. D. Searle & Co.
Sears, Roebuck & Company
Seneca Wire & Manufacturing Company
Serta of Washington, D.C.
Serta of North Carolina
Serta of Georgia
Serta of Buffalo
Serta Mattress Company of Utica, N.Y.
John Sexton & Company
Shampaine Industries, Inc.
Shane Uniform Company
Shasta Beverages Company
Shearer Orchards
Shedd-Bartush Foods, Inc.
Sheldon Wood Products, Inc.
Sigma Chemical Company
David Simmonds Company
Joe J. Simmons Company
J. R. Simplot Company
Sinclair Refining Company
J. Sklar Manufacturing Company

Skookum Packer's Association
Allen V. Smith, Inc.
Smith, Kline & French Laboratories
Smith & Underwood
Smith & Wesson, Inc.
The J. M. Smucker Company
Snake River Trout Company
M. Snower & Company
M. L. Snyder & Son, Inc.
Sorenson Company
Soundscriber Corporation
Southern Fruit Distributors, Inc.
Sparta Brush Company
Spiegel Farms, Inc.
Springer Publishing Company
Springfield Green Industries, Inc.
E. R. Squibb & Sons
St. Regis Paper Company
Stadelman Fruit Company
A. E. Staley Manufacturing Company
Standard Felt Company
Standard Vanilla Company
Stanislaus Food Products Company
Star Dental Manufacturing Company Inc.
Star-Kist Foods, Inc.
Starr Foods, Inc.
Stayton Canning Company
Stein Hall & Company
Steiner Corporation
Sterilon Corporation
J. P. Stevens & Company, Inc.
Stokley-Van Camp, Inc.
Storz Instrument Company
Strand Fruit & Storage Company
Strasenburgh Laboratories
Charles G. Summers, Jr., Inc.
Summit Laboratories
Sun Garden Packing Company
Sun Maid Raisin Growers of California
Sun Shipbuilding & Drydock Co., Inc.
Sunland Sales Cooperative Association
Sunkist Growers, Inc.
Sunshine Biscuit, Inc.
Surgident, Ltd.
Sutures, Inc.
Sweden Freezers Manufacturing Company
Sweetheart Cup Company
Swift Motion Picture Laboratories, Inc.
Switlick Parachute Company, Inc.
Syntex Laboratories, Inc.

T. P. Laboratories
Dan Tames
Taylor Instrument Companies
Teaching Materials Corporation
Teca Corporation
Technical Operations, Inc.
Technicon Company, Inc.
Telescope Folding Furniture Company
Teletype Corporation
Texas Pharmaceutical Company
Thayer Laboratories
Theatre Network Television, Inc.
Thermolyne Corporation
Thermopatch, Inc.
Arthur H. Thomas Company
Charles C. Thomas Company
Thornley & Pitt Company
Thornton Canning Company

Tillie Lewis Foods, Inc.
Toby's Instrument Company
Todd Shipyards
Tonasket United Growers
Tonasket Wenoka Growers
The Torit Corporation
Torrington Company
Torsion Balance Company
J. C. Tracy & Company
Transparent Industrial Envelopes
Travenol Laboratories
Traverse City Canning Company
TreeSweet Products Company
Tri-Ex Tower Corporation
Tri Valley Growers
Tri Valley Packing Association
Trinity Bag & Paper Co., Inc.
Tubbs Cordage Company
Tupperware Home Parties
Turco Products, Inc.
Turlock Cooperative Growers
The Turner Company

Ultra-Violet Products, Inc.
Umatilla Canning Company
Uncle Ben's, Inc.
Union Broach Company, Inc.
Union Carbide Corporation
Union Sugar Company
Uni-Tech Chemical Manufacturing Company
United Biscuit Company
United Fresh Fruit & Vegetable Association
United Growers, Inc.
United Instant Coffee Company
Universal Metal Products
University Film Service
University of Iowa
University of Oklahoma
The Upjohn Company
Urb Products Corporation
Urocon, Inc.
U.S. Borax & Chemical Corporation
U.S. Catheter & Instrument Corporation
U.S. Cold Storage Company
U.S. Detergents
U.S. Industries
U.S. P. Corporation
U.S. Pumice Supply Company
U.S. Rubber Corporation
U.S. Stoneware Company
U.S. Vitamin & Pharmaceutical Corporation
Utah-Idaho Sugar Company

Van Camp Sea Food Company
Van Leer Chocolate Corporation
Van Waters & Rogers, Inc.
Veede-Root, Inc.
Vegetable Oil Products, Inc.
Vermont Rehabilitation Center
Victoreen Instrument Company
Viewlex, Inc.
Viso Corporation
Vita Food Products, Inc.
Vitamix Pharmaceuticals, Inc.
Vlasic Food Products Company
The Vollrath Company

W. T. S. Pharmaceuticals

Walker Laboratories
Wallace Laboratories
Wampole Laboratories
Warner-Lambert Pharmaceutical Company
Warren-Teed Pharmaceuticals, Inc.
Washington Apple Growers Association
Washington Fish & Oyster Company of California
Washington Fruit Growers
Washington Fruit & Produce Company
Washington-Oregon-Idaho Foods
Waukesha Foundry Company
WBBM-TV (Chicago, Ill.)
Welch-Allyn, Inc.
Welch Apples, Inc.
James O. Welch Company
Weller Electric Corporation
Wells & Wade Fruit Company
Wenatchee Beebe Orchard Company
Wenatches Wenoka Growers Association
Wesson Oil & Snowdrift Sales Company
Western California Fish Canners
Western Rubber Company
Westward Dental Products
Westwood Pharmaceuticals
Wexler Film Productions
Weyerhouser Company
T. C. Wheaton Company
Whip-Mix Corporation
White Candy Company
S. S. White Dental Manufacturing Company
White Laboratories

Widmer's Wine Cellars, Inc.
John Wiley & Sons, Inc.
Wilkes-Barre Kiwanis Wheel Chair Club
Will Corporation
Will Ross, Inc.
Will Scientific
J. B. Williams Company
Williams Fruit Company
Williams Gold Refining Company
Williams Optical Company
Williams & Wilkins Company
Williamsburg Millwork Corporation
Willys Motors, Inc.
Wilmot Castle Company
Frank M. Wilson Company
Wilson Lumber Company
Charles S. Wilson Memorial Hospital
Winthrop Laboratories
The Witt Company
Wood Canning Company
F. G. Wool Packing Company
Wright Manufacturing Company
Wyeth Laboratories

Yakima Fruit & Cold Storage
Yakima Fruit Growers Association
Yale & Town, Inc.
Year Book Medical Publishers
Yellow Springs Instrument Company
Young Dental Manufacturing Company

Zenith Radio Corporation
Zimmer Manufacturing Company
Zuckerman-Honickman, Inc.